STARS AND GALAXIES

Birth, Ageing, and Death in the Universe

Based on a Symposium Sponsored by

THE AMERICAN ASTRONOMICAL SOCIETY AND THE FRONTIERS OF SCIENCE FOUNDATION OF OKLAHOMA

Edited by Thornton Page

STARS AND GALAXIES

Birth, Ageing, and Death in the Universe

Thornton Page

Leo Goldberg

Armin J. Deutsch

Marshal H. Wrubel

George O. Abell

Ronald N. Bracewell

Margaret Burbidge

A Spectrum Book

PRENTICE-HALL, INC., ENGLEWOOD CLIFFS, N.J.

PRINTED IN THE UNITED STATES OF AMERICA

84053-C

THE AUTHORS

THORNTON PAGE, Editor. *Fisk Professor of Astronomy; Director, Van Vleck Observatory, Wesleyan University, Middletown, Connecticut.* A teacher who studies the spectra of nebulae and galaxies, and the masses of galaxies.

LEO GOLDBERG. *Higgins Professor of Astronomy, Harvard University; Associate Director, Smithsonian Astrophysical Observatory, Cambridge, Massachusetts.* A supervisor of many research projects, teacher, and expert on infrared spectra and the physics of sun, stars, and nebulae.

ARMIN J. DEUTSCH. *Astronomer, Mount Wilson and Palomar Observatories, Carnegie Institution of Washington; California Institute of Technology, Pasadena, California.* An expert on the spectra of stars, recognized for his studies of the outer layers of stars and of how stars lose mass.

MARSHAL H. WRUBEL. *Professor of Astronomy, Indiana University, Bloomington, Indiana.* A teacher and expert on the mathematical and physical theory of stellar models, and on the application of electronic computing machines to these models.

GEORGE O. ABELL. *Associate Professor of Astronomy, University of California, Los Angeles, California.* A teacher and expert on groups and clusters of galaxies, their distribution, and the bearing of such observations on theories of cosmology.

RONALD N. BRACEWELL. *Professor of Electrical Engineering; Director, Radio Astronomy Institute, Stanford University, Stanford, California.* Designer of radio telescopes, expert in their use, and in the physics of the sun, the atmosphere, and the tenuous gas between the stars.

MARGARET BURBIDGE. *Research Astronomer, University of California, San Diego, California.* Expert in observing and interpreting the spectra of galaxies. Wife of another English astrophysicist with whom she has worked on the relative abundances of the chemical elements in stars, on theories of the formation of these elements, and on the evolution of galaxies.

PREFACE

As part of its program to encourage young scientists, the Frontiers of Science Foundation of Oklahoma, Inc., held a symposium in Oklahoma City on 21 April 1961, to which selected students and science teachers were invited. The speakers and their topics were selected by the Committee on Education in Astronomy of the American Astronomical Society to represent the most active and interesting areas of current astronomical research. These speakers, each recognized by other astronomers as expert in his field, were thus brought together to write this book. Each has described in simple terms the present state of knowledge and technique, with emphasis on how astronomical knowledge was obtained, how it may be extended, and the basic assumptions on which it rests.

The authors come from widely separated institutions, and the variety of their activities is characteristic of some 2,000 astronomers now active throughout the world. There are far too few astronomers for today's needs, and we hope that this book will interest others in the excitement of astronomical exploration.

T. P.

TABLE OF CONTENTS

LIST OF FIGURES

xi

STARS AND GALAXIES

Birth, Ageing, and Death in the Universe

I

Man's Place in Space and Time

Thornton Page

It has taken man a long time to recognize his place in the universe, primarily because his thinking is so self-centered. When we look at the stars on a clear night, it is most natural for us, as it was for the early Greeks 3,000 years ago, to see them as bright spots on a huge globe around us—the "celestial sphere" —with ourselves at the center.

This concept (see *Figure I-1*), which is still quite useful to astronomers, is an anthropocentric one ("man at the center"). It was clearly described by Claudius Ptolemy in his book, the *Almagest*, about 150 A.D. As he says, if you watch the clear sky for several hours, you see that it "turns like a sphere" around a point that is called the celestial pole and which is near the pole star, Polaris, about half way up the northern sky. The stars near this pole move during the night in small circles (*Figure I-2*), and the ones farther away in larger circles, always retaining their relative positions, like spots fixed on the celestial sphere. This big globe turns constantly and regularly, from east to west, making one complete turn in 24 hours.

If you travel northward (*Figure I-3*), you find that your view of the celestial sphere changes—the pole is higher in the sky. This was Ptolemy's reason for saying that the earth, which seems so large to us, is a small sphere at the center of the much larger celestial sphere. As we move around on the earth, the direction we call "up" points in different directions in space.

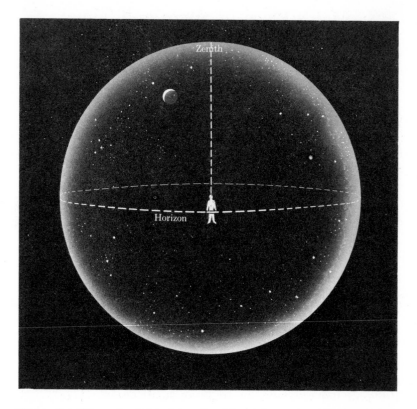

Figure I-1. The celestial sphere. In this anthropocentric concept of the sky the stars were merely spots on a vast sphere rotating once every 24 hours around the earth.

Figure I-2. Apparent motion of stars around the north celestial pole.
This artist's conception represents what might be photographed by
a camera pointed north through a long winter's night.

Motion of the Sky or of the Earth?

You see that *spheres* keep coming into this description.
Because the sphere represented mathematical perfection to
geometers, it was natural for Ptolemy (and earlier Greek astronomers) to assume that everything in the sky—everything
in the universe—had to be spherical, and had to move as
spheres geared to one another would. The moon, for instance,
looks spherical. Since it moves around the sky at a rate different

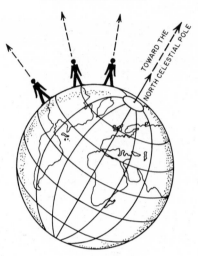

Figure I-3. The different views from different latitudes on the earth. As you go north, the direction "up" changes because the earth is round, and you see the north celestial pole higher in the sky.

from that of the stars, Ptolemy reckoned that it was carried by an invisible sphere smaller than the celestial sphere, but geared to it. He pictured the sun, which also moves among the stars, once around the sky in a year, as carried on a sphere with a different gearing. But what complicated Ptolemy's theory was the observed motion of the planets in loops among the stars (*Figure I-4*), which he had to explain in terms of a set of spheres, all inside the celestial sphere, and geared together in a complicated way (*Figure I-5*).

For more than twelve centuries men accepted this picture, the Ptolemaic theory of the universe. It was agreed that our earth was fixed in the exact center of a vast and complicated set of ethereal spheres. No one could conceive that the firm, solid earth could be moving. Then, during the late 1500's, Copernicus, Kepler, and Galileo changed the picture radically by interpreting most of these motions in the sky as reflections of the earth's own motion. It is easy to see that the apparent daily rotation of the celestial sphere carrying the stars from east to west around the small, spherical earth at the center can be replaced by an eastward rotation of the earth (carrying us with it), the stars being fixed and at very large distances from us. Similarly, the yearly apparent motion of the sun around the sky is a reflection of the earth's real motion around the sun, and the apparent looping motion of a planet like Mars is a reflection (against the background of distant stars) of the earth's catching up on Mars and passing it, as both move round the sun (*Figure I-6*).

The "revolutionary" idea of Copernicus', that man and his earth were *not* at the center of the universe, but were spinning

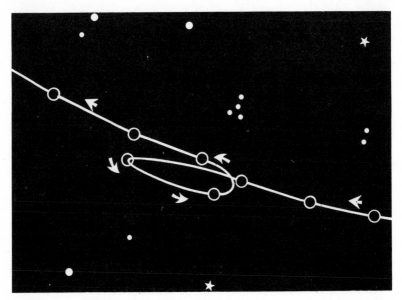

Figure I-4. Looping motion of a planet such as Mars. Positions of a planet plotted on a star map often show a loop like this. Copernicus' explanation differs radically from Ptolemy's.

around the sun along with the other planets, brought a radical change to the ideas of theologians and philosophers. It was soon beautifully confirmed by Isaac Newton, who explained the whole system by an assumed force of gravitation and rules (or formulas, or "laws") for the movement of material bodies when

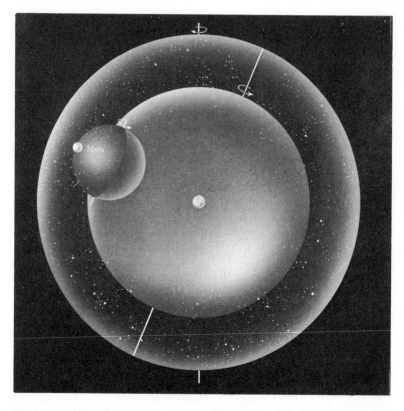

Figure I-5. The Ptolemaic system. This artist's conception shows the celestial sphere, outermost, rotating westward and carrying with it other rotating spheres that were thought to explain the motions of a planet as seen by an observer in the center.

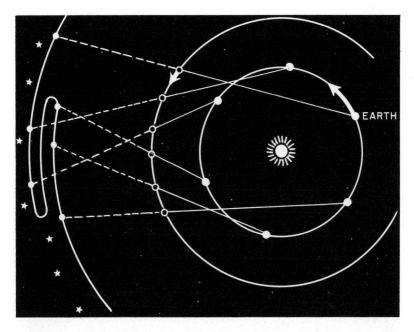

Figure I-6. Explanation of a planet's motion as seen from the earth.
Both earth and planet are moving around the sun, and the difference
in their speed causes "looping" among the stars (which are much
farther away than shown to the left on this diagram).

pulled by a force. Copernicus gets credit for changing man's
anthropocentric ideas—for destroying the idea that we and our
little earth are at the center of the universe—and Newton gets
credit for bringing order to our thinking about motions—for
showing that the moon, planets, apples, missiles, and stars are
moved by forces, all according to the same laws. And these laws,
or formulas, together with simple geometry and a few observations, can be used to show that we on the earth are about 93
million miles from the sun, going around it at 18.6 miles per
second in a path or orbit that is roughly circular.

7

Distances to the Stars

From this planetary merry-go-round we view the stars. Our view changes slightly as we move from one side of the sun to the other, and this change in viewpoint allows us to measure the distances of some of the stars by simple triangulation (*Figure*

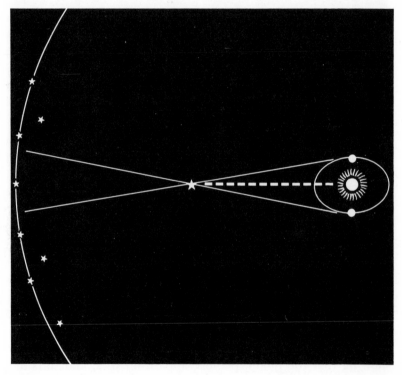

Figure I-7. Measurement of the distance to a star. The nearer star (center) seems to shift position among the more distant stars (left) as the earth moves from one side of the sun to the other (right) in half a year. Actually the stars are all very much farther away from us than this diagram shows—over two hundred thousand times farther than the sun.

I-7). These nearer stars are all so far away that astronomers cannot conveniently use miles as units of distance; instead, we use "light-years" and "parsecs"—units of about 10,000 billion miles —and we find that the nearest stars are several light-years away.

If the sun were that far from us—some 200,000 times farther than it is now—it would be about as bright as many of the stars we see. Moreover, the light from an average star is something like the light from the sun in its color composition, and it is thus established that the stars are simply distant suns, some much brighter than our sun, and some fainter. Also, their temperatures differ; the blue ones are as hot as 100,000° F.; the sun is about 10,000° F., and redder stars are cooler. Knowing the distances from triangulation, we can calculate the stars' absolute brightnesses and say "this blue star is as bright as 1,000 suns, 200 light-years away; that red star is half as bright as one sun, 10 light-years away," and so on.

An interesting and useful discovery was that blue stars are almost all between 200 and 2,000 times as bright as the sun. So if we see a faint blue star in the sky, we know it must be thousands of light-years away. In this way, the astronomer measures larger and larger distances, using nothing more than a consequence of geometry; knowing how bright a star *really* is from its type (that is, its color, or spectrum), and how bright it *appears* to be, we can calculate how far away it is.

Our Galaxy, the Milky Way

Now, when we plot the positions of stars around us, we find that they are not scattered at random. In fact, you can easily see, on a clear night, a concentration of faint stars in a band, the Milky Way, stretching completely around the sky, like a ribbon tied around the celestial sphere. You can see the individual stars only through a telescope, and they are so faint that they must be thousands and tens of thousands of light-years away. *Figure I-8* shows a small portion of the Milky Way in the constellation of Sagittarius.

About 200 years ago the English astronomer, Herschel, reasoned from this band of stars around the sky that our sun must be in a huge pancake of stars, so that we see more stars as we look out in the directions toward the edge of the pancake than if we look perpendicularly through it. Are we at the center of this pancake—the Milky Way Galaxy, as it is now called? No, this system of stars is no more anthropocentric than the solar system; we are located about half way out toward one edge.

Figure I-9 is a schematic side view of our Milky Way Galaxy; not every star is plotted—it would be difficult to draw 100 billion points on the diagram. In any case, we can't see *all* the stars in this gigantic pancake because of obscuring dust clouds that show as dark areas on *Figure I-8*. The over-all size of the galaxy and the distance from our sun to the center were found only 40 years ago by Harlow Shapley, who measured the distances of globular clusters—tightly packed groups of 50,000 stars or more —that are shown in *Figure I-9* by the heavy dots. These clusters are all on one side of us, and Shapley reasoned that gravitational attraction would cause them to be grouped around the center of the galaxy.

But how can all these stars stay spread out in a pancake? According to Newton they are all pulling on each other by gravitational force; you would expect from his laws that they would all fall into the center. Actually, what keeps the stars spread out is the rotation of the Milky Way Galaxy; all the stars are moving around the center just as the planets move around the sun.

This motion, the "galactic rotation," can be measured by an effect of motion on light called the Doppler shift. When a star is moving toward us, its light is a little bluer than normal;

Figure I-8. Part of the Milky Way, photographed with a small lens.
A larger telescope shows that the bright regions are mostly made up
of faint stars. The dark markings are due to interstellar material
blocking our view.   *Mount Wilson and Palomar Observatories*

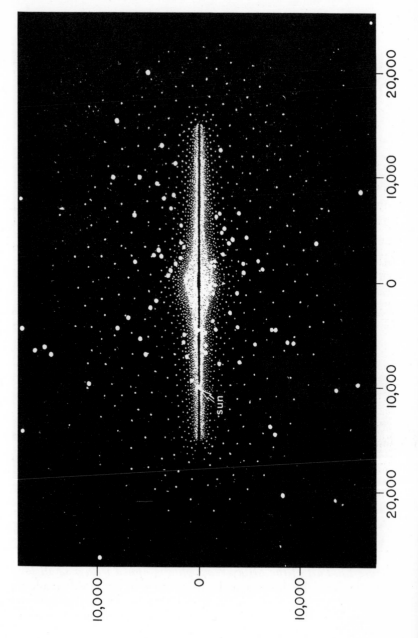

sun

when one is moving away, a little redder. Thus, the actual speed in the line of sight can be measured quite accurately. In this way, the Dutch astronomer, Oort, found in 1924 that all the stars near the sun are moving at about 200 miles per second around the center of the Milky Way Galaxy. Even at this high speed, it will take 250 million years to go around once, and we do not go very far in our lifetime—nor can we really *see* this rotation; it is too slow to change our view of the universe.

This picture of our Milky Way Galaxy was supported and confirmed by the sight of other galaxies that show up in un-cluttered parts of the sky. There are many, many others, like the ones shown in *Figures I-10* and *I-11*. Many of them are spiral in shape, and from this came the idea that they are rotating. Some are seen in edge view, looking very much like the diagram of our Milky Way Galaxy in *Figure I-9*. They are seen in all directions—more and more as we look farther and farther (by using bigger and bigger telescopes). Are we in the center of some vast cloud of these islands of stars? That question comes up in Chapter V, and there you will find that Copernicus' reasoning still applies.

Our Place in Time

Now you see roughly where you stand in the universe—on a small planet going around an average star which is itself one of about 100 billion stars in the slowly rotating Milky Way Galaxy. What about our place in *time?* Have these motions

---

Figure I-9. Diagram of our Milky Way Galaxy, edge-on view. The large dots are measured positions of globular clusters; the distribution of small dots represents schematically the distribution of individual stars. Distances measured along the edges are in parsecs.

Yerkes Observatory

Figure I-10. An open spiral galaxy in Eridanus, NGC 1300. Its shape gives an impression of rotation, but since it takes hundreds of millions of years to turn once around, we cannot hope to detect changes in this view during one man's lifetime, or even during the whole history of astronomy. *Mount Wilson and Palomar Observatories*

been going on for a few thousand years? a few million? a few billion?

In 1650 Bishop Ussher dated the Creation from the genealogy given in the Bible at 4004 B.C.; for a long time (even for some people today) this was accepted as "gospel truth." However, if you accept a miracle such as this, what's wrong with creation 5 minutes ago? It would be scarcely more difficult for the Creator to create all of us sitting here, with our memories of events that never really happened, with our worn shoes that were never really new, with spots of soup that were never really spilled on our ties, and so on. Such a beginning is logically possible, but extremely hard to believe!

Geologists have uncovered a great deal of evidence like the worn shoes and soup-spotted ties to show that the earth, at least,

Figure I-11. Spiral galaxy in Coma Berenices, NGC 4565. This galaxy is seen in edge-on view by chance. Compare it with *Figure I-9* to see why the stars of the Milky Way are considered to form a similar object—a galaxy.　　　　*Mount Wilson and Palomar Observatories*

has been in existence a great deal longer than 5 minutes, or 5,000 years, or 5 million years. In fact, it seems that many processes we see going on today have been going on for 4 or 5 billion years of the earth's past history. For instance, rivers are washing away great areas of land, depositing the silt in the sea. And the silt washed into the sea forms new rock, some of which we see has been pushed up to form mountains. Such processes imply in themselves that a very long time is involved, and, with such an understanding, geologists can measure the age of some rocks quite accurately by the products of radioactive decay in them. They also find fossils in the rocks that reveal what fish, plants, and animals lived and died in the ancient seas, their skeletons leaving imprints in the rocks that were later formed.

In this way we know that the earth has been going around the sun, very much as it does today, for at least 3 billion years; that there have been living things for more than 1 billion years; and that evolution of these living things produced man about 2 million years ago.

What happened earlier still? Astronomers find evidence that the universe is much older—that our Milky Way Galaxy has probably been rotating for 5 or 10 billion years, and that some groups of stars may be 20 billion years old, as you will find out in Chapters IV and VII. But there are many processes that change the stars in much shorter times than this; a hot blue star, for instance, must use up all its nuclear energy in 10 million years or so; other stars called "novae" blow up; still others continually blow off gas into space. Unless there were a counter-process of star formation, the universe would have "aged" drastically in 5 billion years, and there could be no hot blue stars.

The idea of star formation, ageing, and death—"stellar evolution," it is called—is central to much of what follows. The ageing of stars parallels man's life-story as described by Shakespeare in "As You Like It," Act II, scene 7. You will see that the stages of stellar evolution resemble the seven ages of man in Jaques' speech. What we can see of these stages forms the evidence for the ageing of stars, and, in a broader sense, provides some of the variety of the universe, making the stars seem more human and less mechanistic. Stellar evolution lends meaning to questions about the origin of the universe, the galaxy, the sun, or the earth. (In fact, the current theory of the earth's origin associates it with the formation of the sun from a rotating cloud of interstellar gas and dust some 5 billion years ago.)

Theories of the Origin

Then where are we in time? Have these generations of stars been going on forever? Was there any beginning, any creation? Very different answers are offered by two schools of scientific thought. The first of these is associated with George Gamow, a noted physicist-astronomer and popular author, who has developed a theory based on the curved geometry of relativity, the nuclear reactions of physics, the observed motions of galaxies, and the observed abundance of chemical elements in stars. He suggests that everything started with a "big bang" about 10 billion years ago; ever since then, the universe has been expanding and "running down;" that is, its over-all condition has been changing.

The other school, led by Fred Hoyle, an astrophysicist at Cambridge University in England, starts with an extension of Copernicus' idea: we cannot be in the "center" of the universe, or in any unusual position, *nor can we be living at any unusual time* in the history of the universe. This added clause means, of course, that the universe *cannot change in time,* over-all. Stars are born, but an equal number die; galaxies move away from us, but an equal amount of new matter must be created to keep the average density constant.

Thus Hoyle assumes a "steady-state universe" with no beginning and no end; the earth was formed 5 billion years ago, life started, man evolved. Some day the sun will die, ending earth and man's existence; but other stars, other planets, other life, and other races of men are evolving all along, so that the net effect is changeless.

The contrast between these two recent theories—the "Big-Bang" Theory of Gamow and the "Steady-State" Theory of Hoyle—shows how the science of astronomy borders on philosophy, and deals with basic assumptions and beliefs. However, these theories are important to scientists for another reason: they provide a framework into which observations and experimental data can be fitted. Many astronomers are therefore searching for evidence that may help decide between big bang and steady state, as the rest of this book will show.

II

Means of Observation

Leo Goldberg

Astronomy is basically an "observational science." With the exception of what we have learned from the few meteorites that have landed on the earth, everything we know about the external universe has been discovered by observation over very great distances. In astronomy we have no control over the objects we observe, as the physicists do in their laboratory experiments. A noted astronomer from the Soviet Union, Dr. Alla Massevitch, recently said that with the advent of space vehicles, astronomy has become an experimental science also. What she means, of course, is that we now can place artificial planets and artificial moons in orbits; to some extent we can control the sizes and shapes of these orbits, and therefore carry out "experiments." But even if our ability to go out into space were to exceed our wildest dreams, we still will not get much beyond the confines of the solar system in the foreseeable future. Even if we were to put an observatory on the planet Pluto, we would not be appreciably closer to the stars and the galaxies than we are here on earth. This is because the stars are so very far away as compared with the sun and other planets. In a model scaled to show the earth just one inch from the sun, the nearest star would be three or four miles away and the distant galaxies millions of miles away! Even though we land men on the moon and the planets, astronomy will remain an observational science, based on our observations of radiation, chiefly in the form of light, from the distant stars and galaxies.

Light can be thought of as a wave motion that travels through space, and each color has a characteristic wavelength (the distance between two successive peaks of the waves). Radiation includes many different wavelengths: the wavelength of visible light is about a 50-thousandth of an inch, and X-rays have wavelengths as short as a few billionths of an inch. On the other hand, radio waves, which are also emitted by stars and galaxies, have wavelengths measured in fractions of an inch up to many yards.

Effects of the Earth's Atmosphere

Astronomical observations from the surface of the earth are carried out under something of a handicap because the earth is surrounded by a thick blanket of air, which is always turbulent and rather dirty. This air absorbs most of the radiation that comes from the stars and galaxies. The spectrum of radiation (*Figure II-1*) begins with very short gamma rays and, at successively longer wavelengths, includes X-rays, ultraviolet, visible, infrared, short-wave radio, and long-wave radio waves. But the earth's atmosphere allows only two relatively narrow bands of wavelengths to pass through; it blocks all the X-rays, most of the ultraviolet rays, and most of the infrared rays.

Visible light, of course, comes through; this region of the spectrum is a "window" through which we can see the outside universe. At longer wavelengths, called short radio waves, there

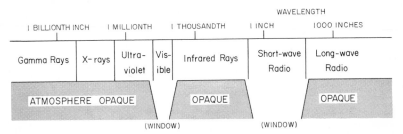

WAVELENGTH

| I BILLIONTH INCH | I MILLIONTH | I THOUSANDTH | I INCH | 1000 INCHES |

| Gamma Rays | X-rays | Ultra-violet | Vis-ible | Infrared Rays | Short-wave Radio | Long-wave Radio |

ATMOSPHERE OPAQUE   OPAQUE   OPAQUE

(WINDOW)   (WINDOW)

Figure II-1. Atmospheric windows in the electromagnetic spectrum.
Physicists are familiar in theory and experiment with the radiations
named above, but the atmosphere blocks all but visible light and
short radio waves coming from the outside.

is another "window" in the atmosphere, and we have learned a
great deal about the universe from the radio waves that come
through this window. Still longer radio waves are turned back
by the atmosphere, and we cannot observe them. It is through
these two windows that man has so far observed the universe
and obtained his present knowledge by using various types of
telescopes.

Optical Telescopes: Refractors, Reflectors, and Schmidt-Type Telescopes

The telescope has three purposes. First, it is a collector
of radiation. The human eye collects only the light falling on its
pupil, which is about two tenths of an inch in diameter. The
largest optical telescope collects light over a two-hundred-inch
circle and brings all of this radiation to a sharp focus where we
can look at it or photograph it, or measure it with a sensitive
photoelectric detector.

The second function of a telescope is to resolve, or separate,
objects that are very close together. The resolving power of a
telescope depends on the diameter of the collecting lens or mir-

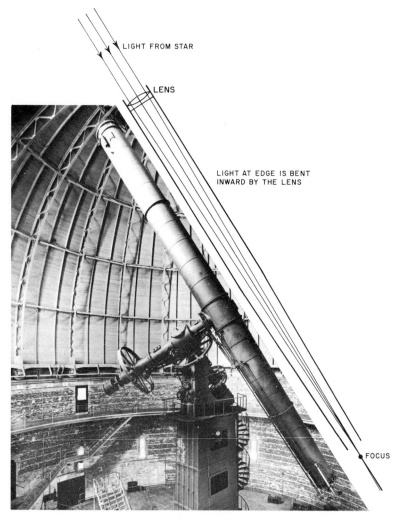

LIGHT FROM STAR

LENS

LIGHT AT EDGE IS BENT
INWARD BY THE LENS

FOCUS

Figure II-2. The 40-inch telescope at the Yerkes Observatory. This is the world's largest refractor. The line drawing shows how the double lens at the upper end refracts light-rays so that they all come to a focus at the lower end.

Yerkes Observatory

ror. For example, a telescope five inches in diameter can resolve two objects that are one second of arc apart. A second of arc is a very small unit of angular measure. A man six feet tall would subtend an angle of one second of arc at 200 miles, so we could stand in Oklahoma City with a five-inch telescope and just be able to distinguish between the head and feet of a man in Fort Worth.

A third characteristic of a telescope is its magnifying power. The magnifying power of a telescope depends on its focal length; that is, the longer the telescope the greater is its magnification, and this is important for studying fine details.

There are basically two different types of optical telescopes: the refractor (*Figure II-2*) and the reflector (*Figure II-3*). In a refractor, light from a star passes through a lens which bends the edge rays so that they come to a focus. The largest refracting telescope ever made is the 40-inch telescope of the Yerkes Observatory in southern Wisconsin. It has not been feasible to make lenses larger than this because the lens must be of perfect quality throughout its interior. Another difficulty is that the lens must be supported by its edge; a very large lens tends to sag under its own weight.

The largest telescopes are the reflecting type, which have a curved mirror instead of a lens. As *Figure II-3* shows, the mirror brings the light from a star to a focus in the middle of the upper end of the tube. In the 200-inch telescope an observer is suspended near this point to look at the star or photograph it. In many smaller telescopes secondary mirrors are introduced to allow the observer to look in more conveniently. In the simple "Newtonian form," the light reflected from a main mirror is thrown sideways by a second flat mirror, so that it can be observed at the upper end on the outside of the tube. Another type makes it possible to observe at the lower end of the tube.

In a reflecting telescope only the surface of the mirror need

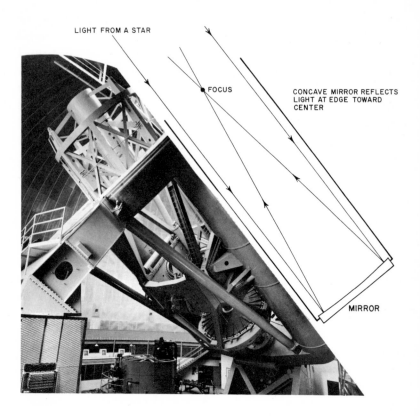

LIGHT FROM A STAR

FOCUS

CONCAVE MIRROR REFLECTS
LIGHT AT EDGE TOWARD
CENTER

MIRROR

Figure II-3. The 200-inch telescope at the Mount Palomar Observatory. The world's largest reflecting telescope consists of an open framework to support optical equipment at the upper left end. The giant mirror (covered) is at the lower right end of the open tube. The large closed tube in the foreground and the two supporting structures are necessary to allow pointing the telescope. The line drawing shows how the mirror reflects light-rays to a focus at the upper left end of the open tube.

Mount Wilson and Palomar Observatories

be perfect, and the mirror can be supported on the back. Thus, reflecting telescopes can be made in very large sizes. One of the largest is the 100-inch telescope at the Mount Wilson Observatory. Our present knowledge of the universe has been derived largely from observations made with this telescope since it was put into operation in 1919. There are now three even larger telescopes in operation: the 104-inch telescope at the Crimean Astrophysical Observatory in the Soviet Union, the 120-inch telescope at the Lick Observatory on Mt. Hamilton in California, and the 200-inch telescope on Mt. Palomar in California.

There is still a third type of telescope which combines advantages of the refractor and the reflector (*Figure II-4*). This is the so-called Schmidt-type telescope, with a mirror at the bottom of the tube and a glass correcting plate at the top. The largest Schmidt-type telescope is also at Mt. Palomar. It has a mirror 72 inches in diameter and a glass correcting plate 48 inches in diameter at the top of the tube.

Generally speaking, accurate measurements of the positions and the motions of stars have been carried out with refractors, whereas measurements of brightness, color, and spectrum, particularly of faint stars and galaxies, have been done with reflectors. One of the most important tasks of modern astronomy is the precise measurement of the color and brightness of stars and galaxies. From such measurements astronomers have put together the life-history of stars—their origin, how they were born, and how they evolved over millions or billions of years. Photographic plates can be used for measurement of brightness or color, but nowadays the most precise measurements are carried out with photoelectric cells. Some of these are so sensitive that, when placed at the focus of the 200-inch telescope, they could easily detect a candle at a distance of about 1,000 miles.

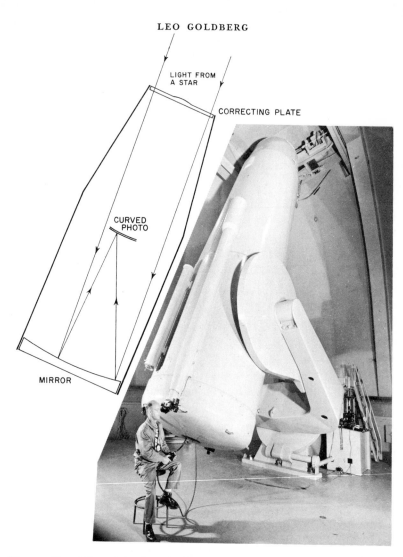

LEO GOLDBERG

LIGHT FROM
A STAR

CORRECTING PLATE

CURVED
PHOTO

MIRROR

Figure II-4. The 48-inch Schmidt telescope at the Mount Palomar Observatory. At the top of the tube a carefully shaped glass plate allows this type of telescope to photograph a large area of the sky in one picture focused on a curved photographic plate near the center of the tube. *Mount Wilson and Palomar Observatories*

The Spectrograph

The most powerful accessory, used on telescopes for nearly 100 years, is the spectroscope (called a spectrograph when it is used with a photographic plate). The components of the spectroscope shown in *Figure II-5* are, first, a slit through which the starlight passes; then a lens followed by a prism or grating that disperses the light into its separate colors, or wavelengths; followed again by a lens which focuses these colors to form a spectrum with red at one end, through all the colors of the rainbow down to the violet and invisible ultraviolet at the other end. The reflection grating is nothing more than a reflecting surface on which parallel grooves have been ruled very close together with a fine diamond—sometimes 15,000 rulings per inch of surface. The different colors or wavelengths of light are reflected off such a surface in different directions.

Laboratory studies and theory have shown that each atom and molecule radiates or absorbs light only at certain wavelengths. In this way the chemical elements familiar on earth have been recognized in stars and galaxies from their spectra. If they were photographed on color film, each of the strips in *Figure II-6* would be colored from red at the right to violet near the left end. Of course, the astronomer does not need to use color film since the same colors always come in the same place in the spectrum.

Stellar spectra carry all kinds of information. *Figure II-6* shows a series of stars of decreasing temperature, hot at the top to cool at the bottom. The dark lines are due to hydrogen, iron, calcium, and other chemical elements. From a knowledge of the structures of atoms and molecules, which comes to us from physics, the spectra of stars and gas clouds can be analyzed to give the abundances of the different kinds of atoms in them, and also the temperature and the pressure of the gases. Accurate

Figure II-5. The Bruce spectrograph of the Yerkes Observatory. This famous old instrument is used on the 40-inch telescope to which it is attached by the large circular ring near the upper right. Light from a star passes through a fine slit at the focus of the telescope, down through a tube (partly hidden in this photograph), through a lens, through the three prisms that can be seen on the left above, and finally through a lens which focuses the spectrum at the upper right end of the black tube at the top. *Yerkes Observatory*

Figure II-6. Spectra of stars. Each strip shows the light of a star spread out from ultraviolet on the left to red on the right. Note the differences between the spectrum of the hot blue star at the top and the spectrum of the cooler red star at the bottom. *Yerkes Observatory*

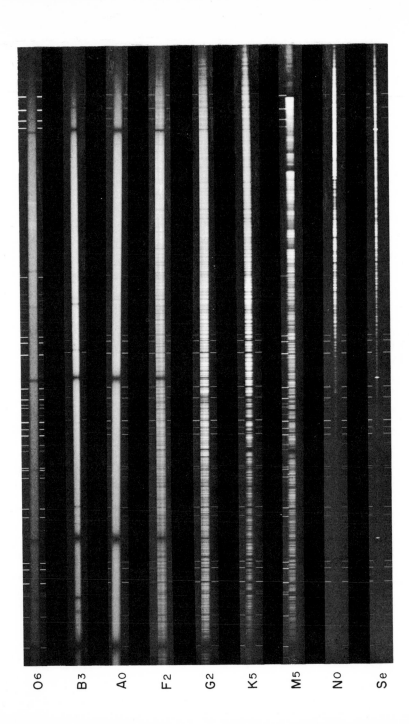

O6　　B3　　A0　　F2　　G2　　K5　　M5　　N0　　Se

measurements of chemical abundances help us understand the origin and the past history of the universe—and all this is done with the spectroscope.

Doppler Shift and Zeeman Effect

The spectroscope also measures the motion of stars. If an atom is at rest, it emits or absorbs radiation very precisely at a fixed wavelength characteristic of that atom. But if the atom is moving toward us, the characteristic wavelength is shifted a little toward shorter wavelengths. If it is moving away from us, the line is shifted a little toward longer wavelengths. This is called the Doppler effect; it is a consequence of the wave nature of light, and allows us to measure the speeds with which stars are moving. *Figure II-7* shows part of the spectrum of the star Arcturus photographed at two different times about six months apart. Above and below are the emission lines in the spectrum of iron photographed at the same time with the same spectrograph. From the pattern of lines you can see that Arcturus contains iron vapor (and other elements), and that the dark absorption lines in the upper star spectrum are displaced toward the right (toward the red), and in the lower star spectrum toward the left (toward the blue). The motion of this star away from us, and six months later toward us, is entirely due to the earth's motion around the sun.

The most spectacular application of the Doppler effect was in the discovery of the expanding universe. If we attach a spectrograph to a large telescope and turn it toward a distant galaxy, we find that there are enormous shifts of the spectrum lines. In *Figure II-8* note the close pair of dark lines in the top spectrum of a fairly bright galaxy. In the next spectrum, the same pair of lines is displaced to the right, and in a still fainter (more distant) galaxy the lines are displaced still farther. In the constellation Hydra there is a galaxy estimated to be at a distance of one billion light-years, which is rushing away from the earth at a speed of about 40,000 miles per second! "The farther away the galaxy, the faster it is receding from us," says the spectrograph—a general statement known as Hubble's Law. The interpretation of this empirical law is covered in Chapter V.

The spectroscope can be used also to discover whether or not stars are magnetized. If atoms radiate or absorb in a magnetic field their lines are split in two, and measurement of the line splittings in the spectra of certain stars shows that they are very highly magnetized, a discovery of Horace Babcock at the Mount Wilson and Palomar Observatories.

Radio Telescopes

From optical telescopes and accessories, we turn now to the other end of the electromagnetic spectrum where the wavelengths are long—the region of radio waves—where there is another "window" in the spectrum of the earth's atmosphere

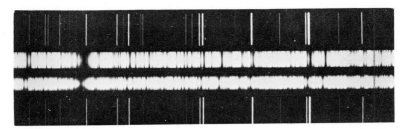

Figure II-7. Doppler shifts in the spectrum of the star, Arcturus. Highly magnified portions of two spectra of Arcturus (in blue-green light only) are shown in the center, with a laboratory spectrum of iron above and below.   *Mount Wilson and Palomar Observatories*

(*Figure II-1*). The radio waves emitted by stars and galaxies are very weak, so we need very large collecting areas. Whereas the largest optical telescope is 200 inches in diameter, the largest radio telescope now planned is 600 feet in diameter. The largest one now in operation, at Jodrell Bank in England, has a diameter of 250 feet. *Figure II-9* shows the 28-foot radio telescope of the University of Michigan. In many ways this particular type of radio telescope is very much like a reflecting optical telescope. The big bowl has a focus out in front where the antenna feed leads the focused radio waves into a radio amplifier. The whole telescope is mounted so that it can rotate to follow the sun or the stars across the sky.

It is not always necessary or desirable to use such a large "dish" for making radio observations. There are other kinds of directional radio antennae; some are nothing more than a pattern of wire like the one in Sydney, Australia (*Figure II-10*), which has the form of a cross 1,500 feet in each direction. An antenna of this type being built in Holland will be about three kilometers long—an entirely different order of size from that of optical telescopes.

What are the advantages of the radio telescope as compared to the optical telescope? One of the difficulties in observing stars at a very great distance is that our galaxy contains great clouds of dust—just like thick smoke that does not allow ordinary light to penetrate. Radio waves pass right through dust and smoke; so radio astronomy has been an important means for studying the structure of our Milky Way Galaxy—a structure that is obscured for optical observations by the interstellar dust. Also, radio telescopes show an entirely new class of objects in the universe that emit very little ordinary light but a high intensity of radio waves. Over 2,000 of these radio sources have been dis-

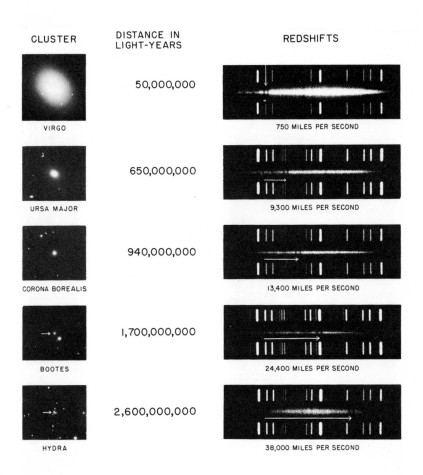

Figure II-8. Hubble's Law of Redshifts in spectra of galaxies. Spectra shown on the right are from the galaxies shown on the left, a relatively near galaxy at the top and a very distant one at the bottom.

Mount Wilson and Palomar Observatories

Figure II-9. The 28-foot radio telescope at the University of Michigan. This early instrument shows the general features of dish-type radio telescopes. Note the inclined axles which allow it to follow a radio star and to be pointed to any part of the sky.

University of Michigan Radio Astronomy Project

Figure II-10. "Mills Cross" radio-telescope antenna in Sydney, Australia. This aerial view shows the two accurately supported, straight wires, each 1,500 feet long, and the instrument shack near their crossing point. *C.S.I.R.O. Radiophysics Division*

covered since radio telescopes came into use about 15 years ago, and they have added an entirely new element to our picture of the universe.

Balloons, Rockets, and Satellites

As pointed out earlier, the earth's atmosphere limits the ability of the astronomer to observe. First, the earth's atmosphere is opaque to all wavelengths except the two "windows" in visible light and short radio waves. Secondly, the earth's atmosphere is turbulent, and tends to smear out fine details that could otherwise be observed. It is possible to get above the turbulence by going to a height of 80,000 feet in a balloon.

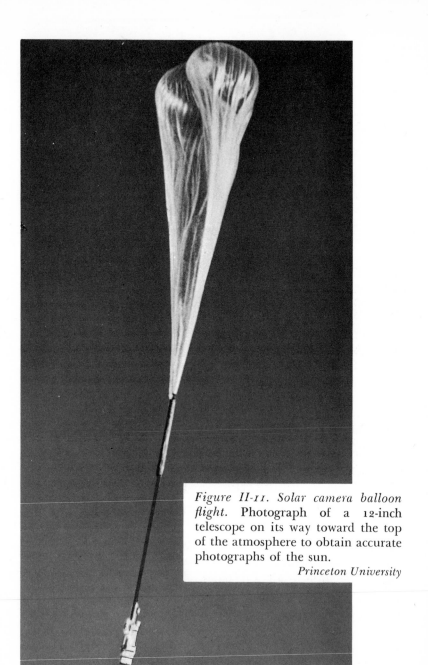

Figure II-11. Solar camera balloon flight. Photograph of a 12-inch telescope on its way toward the top of the atmosphere to obtain accurate photographs of the sun.

Princeton University

Figure II-11 shows one of the flights made recently by Martin Schwarzschild, who obtained some superb photographs of the surface of the sun. One of these is shown in *Figure II-12,* where the solar granulation (the detailed pattern of the sun's surface) is apparent. The dark objects on the left are sunspots. Photographs taken from the surface of the earth show much less detail. In the near future a 36-inch telescope will be used in the same way to make photographs of the planets, stars, and galaxies.

In order to observe the ultraviolet light and X-rays from a star we must go to still higher altitudes—100 miles or more— and this can only be done by means of rockets and satellites.

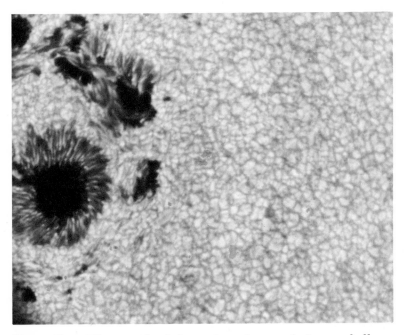

Figure II-12. Photograph of the sun's surface made from a balloon. This remarkably clear picture was obtained on the first Project Stratoscope unmanned balloon flight, under the direction of Martin Schwarzschild.   *Princeton University*

Many observations have been made from rockets shot straight up to spend a few minutes outside the atmosphere. Such a rocket must have a nose cone equipped to point a telescope accurately in a fixed direction.

Orbiting Observatories

In the future most astronomical observations outside the atmosphere will be carried out from artificial satellites which

Figure II-13. S16 Orbiting Solar Observatory. Small jets on four arms are used to control direction (only three are visible). Vanes at the top carry solar cells for the power supply.   *N.A.S.A.*

are not limited to a few minutes of observing time. *Figure II-13* is a photograph of the S16 Orbiting Solar Observatory satellite launched in March 1962 to observe the sun. It is controlled by radio from the ground, and can be made to point accurately in any direction. The observations are recorded on magnetic tape and then sent back to earth by radio.

The most ambitious project of this kind is the National Aeronautics and Space Administration's "Orbiting Astronomical Observatory," expected to be ready for launch in an Atlas Agena rocket some time after 1963. *Figure II-14* shows one model under

Figure II-14. Model of an orbiting astronomical observatory. This satellite will be used primarily for accurate observations of stars, nebulae, and galaxies, unobscured by the earth's atmosphere.

N.A.S.A.

development. One such vehicle, in a project under the direction of Lyman Spitzer at Princeton, will carry a payload of about 5,000 pounds. It will have a fully equipped stellar observatory, complete with a 24- to 30-inch telescope, a spectrograph, and photoelectric cells to measure the intensity of the spectrum. Other groups of astronomers at, for instance, the University of Wisconsin and the Smithsonian Astrophysical Observatory are preparing other types of equipment. One that is being developed at the Kitt Peak National Observatory in Arizona will have a 50-inch telescope, and may be launched into an orbit about 22,000 miles from the earth, where the satellite will go around the earth eastward once in 24 hours, and can therefore hover over one ground station on the earth. A satellite as big as this one can be put into orbit by the Saturn rocket, which is now under development and should be ready by 1963 or 1964.

A possible design is shown in *Figure II-15,* a model of the Saturn rocket with a 50-inch telescope in the nose cone up top. It is unlikely that this very large project can be put into operation before 1968.

Looking still further ahead, astronomers have given serious consideration to the installation of a very large, all-purpose observatory in space, one that would weigh ten to thirty tons. There is a debate going on now as to whether such a space observatory had best be in orbit about the earth, or whether it should be on the moon. So far it is not clear whether the moon offers any substantial advantages for such an observatory as compared with a space station.

What will be the role of men in such a space observatory? Is a man needed to operate the telescope? In the first place, it is certainly possible to operate an observatory satellite on a fully automatic basis, controlled from the earth. Moreover, the presence of a man in an astronomical satellite would actually be a liability: if anything inside the satellite moves,

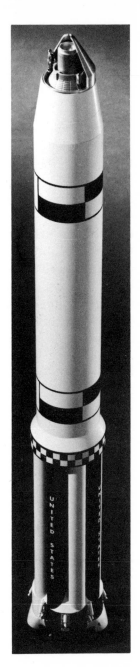

Figure II-15. Model of Saturn rocket with large orbiting astronomical observatory. This project will launch a 50-inch telescope into an orbit high above the earth.

Kitt Peak National Observatory

41

then the satellite itself—even a 30-ton satellite—is set into motion in the opposite direction. Suppose the telescope is pointed at a star and drifts off because the satellite has rotated a bit. When the man leans forward to make a correction he moves the satellite, and it will be absolutely impossible for him to correct the errors that he himself introduces. Of course, if the observatory were on the moon, which is almost as large and unshakeable as the earth, this objection is removed, but men will still have a difficult time living there, with no air, and subjected to lethal bombardment of all sorts. Now that several men have successfully orbited the earth, others will want to go to the moon, and ways will doubtless be found to protect them. There may well be greater need for human observers in other kinds of research, but the astronomical observations we hope for can probably be obtained without men leaving the earth's surface.

From this brief account it should be clear that the means of observation in astronomy are changing rapidly. Never in the past have there been so many exciting opportunities to gain new information about the universe—opportunities that result from developments in technology, especially the advent of space vehicles.

III

The Ageing Stars of the Milky Way

Armin J. Deutsch

Part of what I say here will prove to be wrong. Of course, we do not know what part it will be. Most of this chapter will be substantially correct, but an appreciable part will some day require significant revision, and a small part will turn out to be completely false. This is one of the stimulating characteristics of science: the books are never closed. When we examine questions that are important and difficult, like the question of stellar evolution, we always need more and better information than we have. It will be the astronomers of the next generation who will deepen our present understanding, who will correct the errors that are still undetected, and who will discover the crucially important factors that we have still overlooked.

It is difficult to learn about star ageing because the processes are so slow. On the time scale of human life the stars hardly evolve at all; they just dawdle. During the next six or eight hours you will age relatively much more than the sun has aged during the whole of recorded history.

To illustrate the problem of an astronomer trying to study stellar evolution, let us suppose that a visitor from another planet comes to Oklahoma City to study the evolution of its denizens. We might imagine that on this visitor's home planet there is a fierce scientific controversy raging. One school of thought holds that all residents of Oklahoma City originated at once; they call this the "Big-Bang" Theory. The other school says that Oklahomans are being continually created. Since a typical star has a lifetime about a billion times as long as the life of the astronomer studying its evolution, our hypothetical visitor should observe Oklahoma City for about one billionth the lifetime of a typical resident. This amounts to about two seconds. Oklahoma City is a lively town, but it does not evolve very much in two seconds—and neither do the stars within the lifetime of an astronomer. Even the time available to study the stars during all of recorded history corresponds to only about five minutes' study of changes in Oklahoma City.

So both investigators have to use indirect methods. If our visitor to Oklahoma City had been very assiduous in his five minutes, he might discover that babies are very young human beings and that the people in cemeteries are very old. In fact, he might get a fair idea of the origin, ageing, and death of a typical Oklahoman, although possibly subject to a few serious errors. For example, from his 5-minute look he might conclude that a baby evolves through one stage as a dog and one as an automobile. I wouldn't be a bit surprised if we find ultimately that this resembles our present position with respect to stellar evolution.

The Sun

Figure III-1 is a photograph of the star we know the best, our own sun. It is a typical star, a hot sphere of gas a

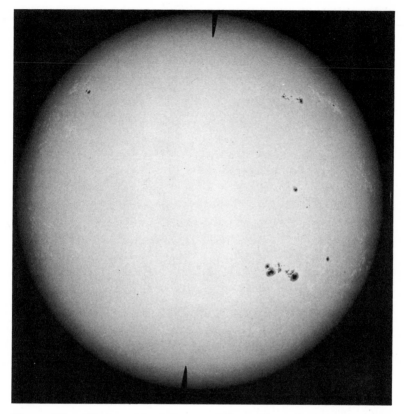

Figure III-1. Photograph of the sun. The surface of our nearest star is at a temperature of about 10,000° F (measured by its color and spectrum), and shows many transient markings.

Mount Wilson and Palomar Observatories

little less than one million miles in diameter, and with about three hundred thousand times as much mass as the earth has. Its visible surface is at a temperature of about 10,000 degrees Fahrenheit, and we calculate that the interior temperature rises steeply toward the center. Radiant energy comes flooding out of the surface of the sun at the rate of about 9,000 horsepower per square foot, and has been doing this through all the billions of years of existence of the solar system. The energy is liberated in the deep interior of the sun by thermonuclear conversion of hydrogen to helium. Every second the sun "burns" 564 million tons of hydrogen into helium, and in doing so it liberates as much energy as the detonation of several billion H-bombs.

Variety Among the Stars

The other stars are similar to the sun, but they are not all identical by any means. Stars, like people, show quite a bit of diversity. As has been mentioned earlier, there are appreciable differences in color, which principally reflect differences in surface temperature. Red stars are relatively cool, and blue stars are the hottest of all, some more than 100,000° F. For a quantitative description of star colors, we measure the ratio of brightness in red light to brightness in blue light. From this ratio we derive a number called the color index of a star.

The brightness of a star is more ambiguous. The brightest star on a photograph is not necessarily the most luminous; it may be actually a star which is intrinsically faint yet looks bright because it happens to be near us. Conversely, some of the stars which are barely visible may be highly luminous, yet look faint because they are very remote.

In order to study the physical properties of the stars we must sort them out with respect to distance. Then, when we come to discuss their intrinsic brightnesses, or luminosities, we can standardize our measures. Figuratively, we put all the stars at some single standard distance; then order begins to appear out of what first seemed to be chaos. We collect measures of the brightnesses of the stars corrected for their different distances, and measures of the colors of the stars. When we plot one against the other *(Figure III-2)*, we begin to discern the laws that govern stellar structure. This kind of a plot is called a Hertzsprung-Russell diagram, or H-R diagram for short. (It is also known as a color-magnitude or C-M diagram.) On *Figure III-2* data are plotted for all known stars within about 150 light-years of the earth.

The Hertzsprung-Russell (H-R) Diagram

The most interesting feature of the H-R diagram is that it shows a relation between the luminosity of a star and its color. For example, some stars on the diagram are several thousand times fainter than the sun, and these stars are also very much redder (i.e., cooler) than the sun is. On the other hand, the stars near the upper left corner of the diagram are nearly a hundred times brighter than the sun, and they are also much whiter (i.e., hotter). If we had surveyed a larger volume of space, we should have found blue-hot stars still more luminous than any plotted in *Figure III-2*.

Most of the stars in the solar neighborhood, then, fall on a diagonal band in the H-R diagram, a band we call the "main sequence." Apparently there are physical laws which require that a star only one-tenth as bright as the sun must have a color somewhat yellower than the sun. It cannot be a red star; it cannot be a blue star; it must be an orange-yellow star. What laws of physics and astrophysics might lead us to expect this?

But we must not oversimplify what the H-R diagram tells us. Although most of the stars lie on the main-sequence band that runs from red stars of low luminosity to blue stars of high luminosity, a few stars are conspicuous exceptions. For instance, one on *Figure III-2* is about one hundred times as luminous as

47

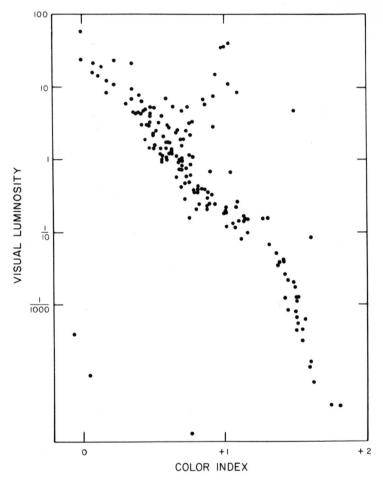

Figure III-2. H-R diagram for nearby stars. The intrinsic brightness of each star is plotted vertically; its color, horizontally, with blue at the left and red at the right. The plotted points for many stars fall along a band, the "main sequence," from upper left to lower right— evidence of a relation between the luminosity and the color of a star.

the sun yet of about the same temperature. "Yellow giant" is the name given to stars off the main sequence in this area of the H-R diagram. There is another group of stars off the main sequence in the lower left which are bluish or whitish but hundreds of times less luminous than the sun. These extremely small stars are called "white dwarfs."

It is as difficult for astronomers to give statistics that are complete as it would be for our hypothetical visitor to Oklahoma City. He might count relatively more children because they make more noise than old folk; we undoubtedly count more of the highly luminous stars because we can see them more easily. The best counts up to the present time would lead us to believe that perhaps 80 or 85 per cent of all the stars are on the main sequence. Another 5 or 10 per cent of the stars are down among the white dwarfs. A smaller fraction lies among the red giants, and a very few are still bigger and more luminous. We call them the "super giants." And maybe a tenth of a per cent of the stars in the sky can't make up their minds what to be. Their brightnesses and temperatures vary; they move around on this diagram. We shall say more about these variable stars later on.

The Mass of a Star

One of the first things that astronomers wanted to know about the main sequence on the H-R diagram was this: What is the real physical difference between a red star of low luminosity and a blue star of high luminosity? This is possible to ascertain owing to the fortunate circumstance that some stars are double stars. What looks to the unaided eye like a single star often turns out in a telescope to be a close pair of stars, and these stars are found to be in motion around each other. The motion is slow, but a number of such stars have been watched as they go completely around their companions. These orbits tell us how the two stars in a pair attract each other. Since the attraction depends upon the masses of the stars (Newton's law of gravitation), studying the orbits of double stars allows us to "weigh" the stars—to find their masses. Such measures show that the masses of stars differ systematically along the main sequence. All the stars that plot near the sun on the main sequence have just one solar mass; the stars plotted down near the lower right, about a quarter. A star forty times as luminous as the sun has nearly three times the mass of the sun, and stars even bluer and more luminous than those shown on this diagram are twenty or even thirty times the mass of the sun.

This is the evidence for an important relation, or astrophysical law: the *mass-luminosity relation,* which states that the more massive a star is, the more brightly it shines; that is, the faster it burns its fuel. The effect is a very striking one; the luminosity of a star depends sensitively on its mass. If the mass of a star is doubled, its luminosity is not just doubled, but multiplied by ten or twelve. This means that the more luminous and more massive stars burn their fuel so very rapidly that they cannot last as long as the less luminous stars. At first this may seem a paradox; the more matter a star has to burn, the less time it can go on burning. As already mentioned, the sun is burning its hydrogen at the rate of 564 million tons a second. There is enough mass in the sun so that it could last at this rate for 50 billion years. But stars that are ten thousand times as luminous as the sun must be burning their hydrogen ten thousand times as fast. Even though these stars have about ten times the sun's mass to start with, they can last only one thousandth as long for a maximum lifetime of only 50 million years—a flash in the pan, astronomically speaking. So there are stars that you can see in the sky which must have come into being much more recently than the earth, some probably even as recently as man. By the same token there must have been many stars in the skies a billion years ago that have exhausted their fuel and faded away.

Stars in Clusters: Evidence of Ageing

Now the astronomer's task is clear. We need not wait long enough to see an individual star change with time; we can infer by indirect arguments which are the young stars, which are the old stars, and what is the course of evolution from birth to middle age to death of a star.

In recent years a great deal of our information about the evolution of stars has come from the studies of star clusters like the one shown in *Figure III-3,* a cluster called Praesepe, or the Bee Hive. There are two important advantages to studying stars in a cluster. First, they are all at about the same distance from us. This is important because, as we have already seen, it is difficult to find out whether a star that looks twice as bright as another has a real difference in luminosity, or is just at a different distance. But we know that if one star looks ten times brighter than another in the same cluster, it really is ten times more luminous, since both are at the same distance. The second advantage is that the stars in a cluster have been together since their birth. There can be little doubt that these stars came into being at the same time; probably they all have the same age.

The fact that stars in this cluster have different luminosities must mean that they have different masses—because of the mass-luminosity law. So here we have a group of stars that had a common origin—at the same place and time—and include a variety of masses. Moreover, other clusters may have different ages, so that differences between them may reveal the process of stellar evolution.

Figure III-4 shows the H-R diagram of this same star cluster,

Figure III-3. A cluster of stars, Praesepe, the "Bee Hive." The stars in this irregular group are close together in space and were probably all formed at one time. Because they are all at about the same distance from us, the H-R diagram can be plotted using measured brightness.
Yerkes Observatory

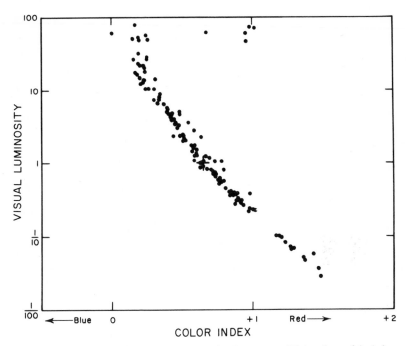

Figure III-4. H-R diagram for stars in Praesepe. This plot of brightness (vertical scale) against color (horizontal scale) refers to the cluster of stars shown in *Figure III-3.* Note the four red giant stars in the upper right, and the lack of blue stars in the upper left.

Praesepe: the measured colors of the stars plotted against their luminosities. The sun would occupy a middle position on the diagram. In the lower right are stars of low mass, low luminosity, low surface temperature. In the upper left we expect the blue stars of high mass, high luminosity, and high surface temperature. But there are no such massive blue stars in this cluster. The most massive stars that appear are about twice the mass of the sun and white in color. Moreover—what is most significant— just at this level of brightness where the main sequence stops, the cluster shows four red giant stars. What happened to the upper part of the normal main sequence? Why are there no blue stars in Praesepe?

In *Figure III-5*, the H-R diagram of another cluster, called Messier 16, we have a very different situation; all of the stars are

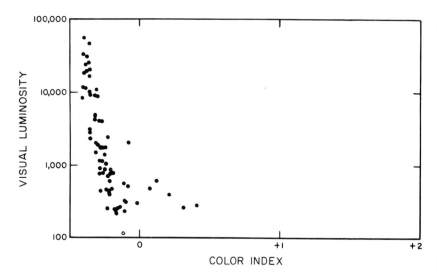

Figure III-5. H-R diagram for stars in the cluster Messier 16. This star cluster includes luminous blue stars (in the upper left of its H-R diagram), which mark it as a much younger cluster than Praesepe (*Figure III-4*).

bluer than those in Praesepe and extremely luminous. In this cluster there are only massive blue stars, and all of the white, yellow, and red ones of lower mass are missing. This cluster has only stars of high luminosity that are burning their hydrogen very rapidly. That means that they have short lifetimes, computed to be just a few tens of millions of years. In 20 or 30 million years many of these stars are going to burn out. They will have used up their hydrogen. Right now, they must be very young.

Birth and Death of a Star

In most cases, clusters of young stars are found to be closely associated with nebulae, which are bright gas clouds and dust clouds. So we conclude that these hot, young, luminous stars must recently have condensed out of the interstellar clouds of dust and gas with which we see them associated. In a cluster like Praesepe where these very young stars are not to be seen, and where we find no dust and gas, any hot massive stars which may once have existed have died. They used up their hydrogen and faded out, and the dust and gas out of which they condensed long, long ago is gone. The only stars left in Praesepe are the less massive ones, which husband their fuel more carefully and have longer lifetimes.

It is possible to compute approximately how long it takes a star of a given mass to exhaust its hydrogen, and by comparing these calculations with the color-magnitude (H-R) diagrams of clusters we can get estimates of the ages of the different star clusters. This has been done in the past few years for a number of clusters, and we find ages ranging from as little as ten or twenty million years to ten or twenty billion years. All through this longer interval of time, clusters of stars have evidently been condensing out of the clouds of dust and gas that we see along the Milky Way. Once the stars are formed, they shine by the conversion of hydrogen into helium until they exhaust their fuel and fade out.

Can we say anything about what happens to a star on its way to extinction? Here, the variable stars play a role: stars that move around on the H-R diagram. They change in brightness and change in color, many with a period of about five days from

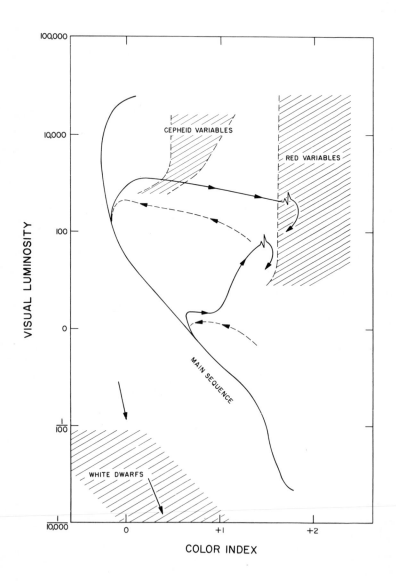

faint to bright and back to faint again. The fact that stars of this kind are rare suggests that a star passes through this stage quickly—it is a short-lived stage in stellar evolution. The observations suggest that when a star nears extinction it moves (on the H-R diagram) off the main sequence toward the region of the giants, passing through a region of instability where it fluctuates in brightness for a little while. Before finally fading out it then spends some time in the region of the red giants, like the four stars in Praesepe (*Figure III-4*).

Figure III-6 summarizes the present view of stellar evolution, shown schematically on an H-R diagram. We know very little about the early stages—about just how a star is born out of the clouds of dust and gas. Theoretical studies show that a condensing cloud of gas and dust begins to shine while it is still quite cool—well off to the right of the main sequence. The forming star heats up as it condenses, moves left on the H-R diagram and onto the main sequence at a point which depends on its mass. If it is a star with a quarter the mass of the sun it will reach the main sequence at the lower right; if it has twice the mass of the sun it will reach the main sequence with 15 times the sun's luminosity, and so on.

Having reached the main sequence it stays there for most of its life, in equilibrium. The physical reasons for this are covered in the next chapter. Then, when the star begins to exhaust its hydrogen, it moves off the main sequence. Near the upper left end, the massive, bright blue giants move off in less than ten million years. First they brighten up, start pulsating, and hence

---

Figure III-6. Evolutionary tracks shown schematically on an H-R diagram. The lines show how the luminosity and color of a star are expected to change with time. Starting on the far right of the H-R diagram, it first grows smaller, hotter, and brighter, until it reaches the main sequence. These changes, and others indicated by arrows on the diagram, take millions to billions of years.

become variables in the region to the right of the main sequence. But they move quickly through that region, stop pulsating, fade a little, and get redder and more bloated—they become cool stars of high luminosity, or "red giants." Then once again they become variable stars, red variable stars, and by this time they are near extinction; their nuclear fires are burning low. Then they somehow get from the red giant region at the upper right down into the region of the white dwarfs at the lower left of the H-R diagram. White dwarfs are the "skeletons" of stars, as explained in the next chapter, and like human skeletons their masses are very much smaller. In order to make the transition from red giant to white dwarf, a star must get rid of a large part of its mass. This process is discussed later on.

Abundances of the Chemical Elements

We must note one other important fact that comes from the kind of spectroscopic studies described in Chapter II on stars in different clusters of various ages. The measured abundances of the chemical elements are nearly the same in all these stars, but not quite the same. In general, the stars in very old clusters differ in chemical composition from the sun and from stars in younger clusters; the metals and other heavier elements are much less abundant relative to hydrogen and helium. It is therefore very likely that when stars were forming 10 or 20 billion years ago, there were fewer heavy atoms in the galaxy than there are now. If this is true, it shows a connection between the evolution of stars in the galaxy and the evolution of the chemical elements themselves. It may show that heavy atoms have been formed from lighter atoms as the galaxy aged.

Referring to *Figure I-9* (the schematic diagram of our Milky Way Galaxy), we should emphasize that the stars and clusters

Figure III-7. A typical globular cluster, Messier 13. About 100 clusters of this type are known, each consisting of 100,000 stars or so. The remarkable symmetry is in marked contrast to the irregular grouping of stars in *Figure III-3*. Globular clusters were used as bright beacons in mapping the galaxy (Chapter I); here we are concerned with their age. *Mount Wilson and Palomar Observatories*

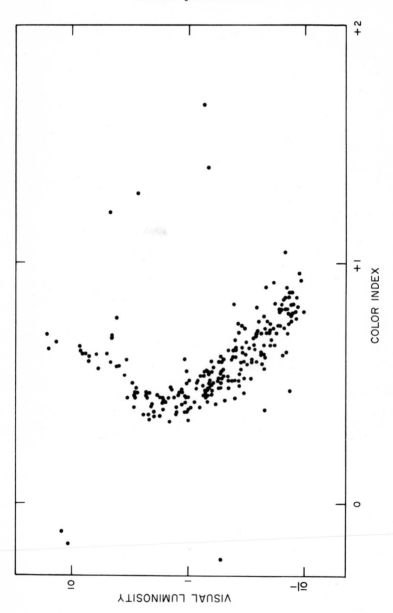

discussed so far in this chapter lie in the central plane of the Milky Way system, very close to the dark central line on *Figure I-9*. They are immersed in clouds of dust in the central plane of the galaxy, and that is where the new stars are being formed. In contrast, the globular clusters, shown by the large white spots on *Figure I-9*, are far from the central plane of the galaxy. They are a different kind of cluster; they seem to avoid the galactic plane; they are moving very fast relative to the stars in the galaxy, and they do not take part in the rotation of the rest of the galaxy.

Figure III-7 is a photograph of a globular cluster, consisting of about one hundred thousand stars. Every star in this photograph is more luminous than the sun. The stars look crowded, and measured Doppler shifts show that they are moving relative to each other with speeds of five or ten miles a second. But the crowding is illusory, and there is little chance of collision. Actually there is about as much crowding here as there would be if you were to drop two or three oranges into the Grand Canyon and let them move around at random.

This globular cluster is typical of the hundred or so known in our galaxy. Part of its H-R diagram is shown in *Figure III-8*. Here, the main sequence is missing from the blue stars through the white stars down to the yellow stars; the main-sequence stars are burned away right down to stars of about the same color as the sun. This cluster must therefore be very old. The white dwarfs cannot be seen because the cluster is so far away and those stars are so faint. But the most interesting point is that the stars in this old globular cluster are very deficient in

---

Figure III-8. H-R diagram of a typical globular cluster, Messier 13. Like all the globular clusters, this shows no blue stars. Even the white stars just above the sun's position on the main sequence are missing. We conclude that such a globular cluster is so very old that all such bright stars have "burned out."

Figure III-9. A supernova gas cloud, the Crab Nebula. In 1054 A.D., a star was observed to shine very brightly for a few months at this position in the sky. Now, over 900 years later, we see (in a telescope) this large cloud of glowing gas and recognize that a violent explosion took place. This supernova explosion blew most of the mass of an old giant star back into space as interstellar gas.

Mount Wilson and Palomar Observatories

heavy atoms. In fact, this is characteristic of stars in most of the globular clusters. Some of them have a hundred times fewer heavy atoms per pound than the sun does, and their ages are estimated at 20 to 25 billion years.

Death by Explosion

Finally, *Figure III-9* shows one way that a red giant may get rid of most of its mass as it changes to a white dwarf. You see here the residue of a catastrophic explosion of a star. When it was observed by Chinese astronomers in the year 1054, the exploding "supernova" was the brightest star in the sky for several months. We still see the explosion continuing today; the expansion of this gas cloud is measured at about six or seven hundred miles a second. In the 900 years since it started, the cloud has expanded to a diameter of about five light-years. Thus we conclude that *Figure III-9* shows the remains of a star which has lived out its life and is now returning most of its substance to the interstellar medium, leaving its skeleton—probably a white dwarf—and this expanding nebula in the graveyard of space.

IV

The Life-Story of a Star

Marshal H. Wrubel

It must be clear by now that an astronomer does not merely sit on a mountaintop gazing at the sky and making notes in his little notebook. The astronomer today has a wide variety of instruments at his disposal—telescopes, spectrographs, photometers, rockets, satellites, and even electronic computers—with which to explore the universe.

In this chapter we shall talk about the work of the theoretical astrophysicist whose job it is to explain the regularities and peculiarities that the observations reveal. A theorist cannot simply propose theories "out of the blue"; he combines the observations with his knowledge of modern physics in the hope of understanding nature. There is a constant interplay between observation and theory. Observations lead to a theory; and, in turn, the theory may indicate some crucial observations that will either support it or prove it to be wrong. When observations disagree with theory, the theorist must go "back to the drawing board." As you will see, even theoretical research in astronomy is far from static.

In the previous chapter you were introduced to the Hertzsprung-Russell or H-R diagram, one of the most compact and useful ways of presenting the results of many observations. The importance of studying star clusters was also emphasized, and it was pointed out that different clusters have different H-R diagrams. We learned of the main sequence along which many of the stars in clusters lie, and also of an observed relation between mass and luminosity for stars along this main sequence. Differences between young and old clusters were mentioned, and also such interesting stars as red giants and white dwarfs. Now we must see if these observations have a theoretical explanation, and if we can fit them all together to follow the "life" of a star.

Inside a Star

Just as an architect makes a model of a building, so the astrophysicist makes mathematical models of stars. But our models are not made of papier mâché; they consist of equations and numbers. We call them *models* because we know that they do not represent the details of a star accurately; but they do represent the principal features, from which we can learn a great deal.

We shall begin at the middle of our story with a star on the main sequence, setting aside for the moment the question of how it got there or where it goes afterward. Let us see if it is possible to reason out what is going on inside such a star.

It is remarkable that we can find out anything about the interior of something as remote and impossible to penetrate as a star. It can be done by extending the laws of laboratory physics to conditions that are quite different from those used in the laboratory—to temperatures of tens of millions of degrees and densities hundreds or thousands of times that of water. We dig into a star with our minds rather than with picks and shovels.

The sun is a good example with which to begin. Our sun is an enormous sphere of hot gas, more than 300,000 times as massive as the earth. Newton's Law of Gravitation tells us that such a massive body will tend to collapse under its own gravitational attraction. Since the sun does not collapse, we know there must be something opposing the gravitational force and balancing it exactly. If the gas inside the sun were hot and dense enough, it could exert a pressure high enough to balance the gravitational force and prevent the sun's collapse. In a precise form, we can express this balance, or *equilibrium,* in terms of mathematical equations using the law of gravitation and the relation between gas pressure, density, temperature, and chemical mixture. We can easily compute that the pressure at the center of the sun must be more than a billion times the air pressure at the surface of the earth. We also find that the temperature of much of the material in the interior of the sun must be measured in millions of degrees in order to exert such a high pressure. However, we cannot find the precise pressure and temperature until we have taken other things into account.

Nuclear Reactions that Keep the Stars Shining

Once we realize that the temperature at the center of the sun is very high, we are on our way toward understanding the source of all the energy that continually pours out of its surface. At such high temperatures, the atoms of a gas (stripped of most of their electrons and therefore called "ions") are dashing about at random with very high velocities. Collisions between these ions are very frequent. Most of the time they bounce off each other, but occasionally they interact in a nuclear reaction which forms a heavier atomic nucleus and releases some energy. If a large enough number of nuclei interact at one time, the amount of energy produced is correspondingly great.

There must be a tremendous amount of nuclear fuel available to keep the sun from burning out. What can it be? The best candidate is hydrogen, because evidence from spectrographs indicates that stars contain more hydrogen than any other element. A careful study of possible nuclear processes involving hydrogen shows that there are two series of reactions that can provide the energy we need at the temperatures we expect. Both have the same final result—four hydrogen nuclei are converted into one helium nucleus—but the details are different.

Why is energy produced when hydrogen is converted to helium? The helium atom is not quite four times as massive as the hydrogen atom; so in the process of making helium out of four hydrogen atoms a little mass (only about seven tenths of a per cent) is left over. This is converted to energy.*

If all the energy radiated by the sun is produced this way, more than five hundred million tons of its hydrogen are being converted to helium every second!

The two series of reactions that can form hydrogen from helium are called the "proton-proton chain" and the "carbon cycle." The first one is the more important reaction at temperatures up to about thirty million degrees Fahrenheit, at which point the other process takes over. In the sun, it is the proton-proton chain that produces the energy, but there are stars in which the carbon cycle is the important one. Both reactions are

---

* The amount of energy, E, resulting from mass m is given by the well-known formula $E = mc^2$, where c is the velocity of light. This formula, a result of Einstein's theoretical work, means that one gram of mass gives 900 billion billion ergs of energy, or one pound gives over 9 million billion calories.

very sensitive to temperature: doubling the temperature increases the energy produced by the proton-proton chain by about 16 times, and that produced by the carbon cycle by 300,000 times!

To continue constructing our model star, we must know precisely how much energy will be produced. This information is supplied by physicists who measure the rates of nuclear reactions in the laboratory by using "accelerators" to hurl atoms together. They can tell us just how much nuclear energy would be produced by a given mixture of elements at any density and temperature; that is, for example, how fast hydrogen is being converted into helium.

Accounting for the production of the energy inside the star is not enough; we have to study how it moves through the star and out into space. The energy, in the form of radiation, will move outward because the center of the star is hotter than the outer parts. Stellar material is not transparent, and it resists the flow of radiation much as a wire resists the flow of an electric current. This resistance, or opacity, also depends on the density, temperature, and chemical mixture.

The greater the opacity, the larger the difference in temperature needed to drive energy through the star. Eventually, the energy reaches the surface and is radiated into space. Now, if more energy were produced in the interior than were radiated, the sun would heat up; and if the reverse were true, it would cool down. Since neither happens, just as much energy must be produced every second as is radiated away. Once again this can be expressed mathematically and added to the mathematical equations of our model.

Once the physicists' data have been assembled and the proper mathematical equations selected, we can construct our model of a star. In this model the gravitation must be balanced by the gas pressure, the nuclear reactions must produce energy at the right rate, and this energy must be able to move out against the opacity. The job is a big one, but it is made much easier by using highspeed electronic computers. After a good deal of work we achieve a model giving the temperature, density, and pressure at every point inside a sphere of gas with the same mass, radius, luminosity, and chemical mixture as stars on the main sequence.

The Expected Relation Between Mass and Luminosity

Let us suppose that we have computed such a model for the sun; you might think that we could make a model for another star just as massive as the sun but brighter or larger. This turns out to be impossible; once the mass and the chemical mixture of the material are specified, the equations of the model *predict* the size and the luminosity of the star.

If we set about computing models for stars of various masses made up of the same material, the predicted stars would have different luminosities and surface temperatures that lie along a line on the H-R diagram similar to the observed main sequence. In other words, the observed relation between luminosity and mass of a star is predicted by this mathematical theory. What is more, the main sequence observed in the H-R diagram of a cluster, therefore, indicates that there are stars of various masses in the cluster, and that probably all the stars of the cluster were originally formed out of the same mixture of chemical elements.

The model we have been talking about is a kind of snapshot of what a star is like at one instant of time; but a star cannot stay on the main sequence forever. The reason is easy to understand: a star has only so much hydrogen, and when that is used up in nuclear reactions, something must happen. As another complication, the hydrogen fuel is not used up equally throughout the star. The nuclear reactions take place fastest at the center, where the temperature is greatest, and gradually helium replaces hydrogen in the central regions. At the temperatures we have been discussing, helium nuclei do not interact; the helium is a kind of "nuclear ash." However, it does change the physical properties of the material in the star. For example, the pressure exerted by helium is less than the pressure of the hydrogen it replaced. The star must readjust to these new conditions. The readjustment may be sudden in some cases, very like the collapse of a bonfire after the underpinnings have burned to ash that cannot support the wood pile.

The Expected Ageing of a Main-Sequence Star

Our first model gave us the temperature and density everywhere inside the main-sequence star. From these we can compute the precise rate at which hydrogen is being converted into helium at every point in the interior. This gives us a new chemical mixture which can be introduced into the computation to give the new structure and new rates of hydrogen burning at a later time in the star's history. The computation can be repeated in this manner step by step to follow the life-story of a star.

When a star begins to evolve away from the main sequence, it moves to the right in the H-R diagram. As explained in Chapter III, the stars at the top of the diagram leave the main sequence soonest because they are consuming hydrogen most rapidly. A star near the top of the main sequence will stay there perhaps only 10 million years; but a star like the sun, quite low in the main sequence, will be on the main sequence for several billion years because it uses its hydrogen fuel very slowly. *Figure IV-1* shows how individual stars move away from the main sequence in the H-R diagram.

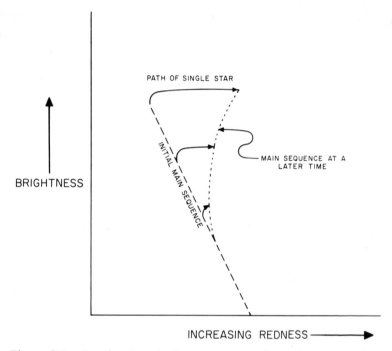

Figure IV-1. Predicted evolution of stars on the main sequence. The calculated brightness-color plots for individual evolving stars move to the right, away from the top of the main sequence. The dashed line represents the main sequence in an H-R diagram of a young cluster, the dotted line the main sequence at a later time, after the stars have aged. Since stars near the top of the main sequence change most rapidly, the main sequence becomes curved to the right as time goes on.

We would very much like to be able to compute the path of any kind of star on *Figure IV-1* in detail, but so far this has not been possible. One successful series of calculations has been carried out by Schwarzschild in America and Hoyle in England for stars a little more massive than the sun. They found that, as the helium content is built up in the interior, the star becomes larger. Surprisingly, however, it does not swell uniformly. Actually, the central parts shrink, releasing gravitational energy, while the outer parts expand. In the H-R diagram the point representing the star moves to the right and up. As the central parts shrink, they gradually heat up and by the time the star reaches the red giant region, the interior is sufficiently hot—over 100 million degrees—to ignite a new fuel. This fuel is helium, the product of the previous hydrogen reaction, which remains inert until this high temperature is reached.

In this new reaction three helium nuclei come together to form carbon. Drastic things must happen when a star starts producing energy from helium. It must rapidly reorganize itself because of the sudden new production of energy in its interior. Schwarzschild has studied this "helium flash" and he finds that the star moves back to the left and down in the H-R diagram, approximately reversing the path that it took on its way up.

Formation of Chemical Elements in the Stars

No one has yet calculated the evolution of the stars beyond this stage, but we have some ideas as to what may happen. It has been proposed by a number of nuclear physicists, in particular the Burbidges, Fowler, and Hoyle, that not only can helium and carbon be formed in the interior of stars, but all the other chemical elements as well. It was pointed out in Chapter III that spectroscopic observations show that very young stars are richer in the metals than very old ones, suggesting that metals have somehow been produced in the galaxy between the birth of the oldest and most recently formed stars. By studying the possible nuclear reactions that can occur at the very high densities and temperatures of giant stars, it may be possible to account for the formation of all the chemical elements, beginning with hydrogen alone.

Several processes must be at work to produce the elements. Some nuclei of the heavier elements can be built by using building blocks of helium; but to go further one must have a source of neutrons.

Even with an adequate source of neutrons, the formation of all the elements is not a simple matter. Some elements can be formed in a slow process, but others require some sort of cataclysm during which neutrons are stuffed into nuclei very rapidly, before they can pop out again.

One rapid process that has been suggested is the explosion of a supernova. *Figure III-9* shows the remnant of one supernova; there are only a few supernovae known in our galaxy, although observations of other galaxies show that they occur about once every three hundred years in any one galaxy.

Why does a supernova explode? Perhaps in its evolution the star becomes very unstable at a time when the models we have been discussing do not apply at all. Processes might then take place in a matter of seconds rather than in thousands or millions or billions of years. In a supernova the heavier chemical elements might be formed during such an explosion and the whole mixture shot off into space like the cloud of gas in *Figure III-9,* spreading the newly formed elements into the interstellar gas. Later generations of stars formed from this interstellar material would then be enriched in the heavy elements; that is, young stars would have more heavy element material than older stars.

This cycle of star formation in a slowly changing mix of the elements is undergoing critical examination by many astronomers today. It brings us to both the beginning and the end of our story. First, for the beginning: the problem we have neglected up to now is how a star reached the main sequence in the first place. We can see (*Figures I-8* and *III-9*) the inter-stellar material from which stars possibly could form, but the details of how some of these gas clouds start to contract and form stars are not clearly understood. Once a cloud starts to contract under its own gravitation, however, we know that it must heat up due to the release of gravitational energy. Henyey and his coworkers in Berkeley, and Cox and Brownlee at Los Alamos have computed this contraction of gas clouds into stars on the main sequence and they have "watched" (on electronic computers) the ignition of nuclear reactions in the interior. Compared to the time a star spends on the main sequence, the contraction phase is relatively short.

White Dwarfs, the Burned-Out Skeletons of Stars

Now for the end of the life-story: the very last stages of a star's history are probably spent as a white dwarf. Strangely, we know more about this very last stage than we do about how a star changes from a red giant to a white dwarf. White dwarfs are observed to be stars of extremely high density; not too different in mass from the sun yet more like the earth in size, with all their material squashed to densities of tons per cubic inch.

Although it has never been observed in the physics laboratory, we nevertheless have a theory for the behavior of such dense material. It is called "degenerate matter"; this means that the electrons are packed as closely together as possible. It is quite unlike ordinary matter, which is mostly empty space. The theory of quantum mechanics predicts how many electrons can be packed into a given space and permits us to describe the be-havior of degenerate material.

When we study spheres of degenerate gas in the same way as

we study models of ordinary stars, by considering the balance of the gas pressure against the gravitational attraction, we find this interesting result: a completely degenerate star cannot be stable with a mass greater than about 1.4 times the mass of the sun. Stars of larger mass cannot "die" without getting rid of the excess material somehow. Perhaps they get rid of it by slow streaming of the material out of the star, as has been observed by Deutsch, or perhaps they get rid of the excess material by a violent explosion, as a supernova does.

In any case, by the time it has become a white dwarf, a star will have practically exhausted its nuclear energy sources. A white dwarf simply radiates away its heat energy, and gradually cools down. It remains in the lower left of the H-R diagram for a very long time, but eventually cools to oblivion. The mass of material is still there, but it does not radiate any more. That is, it ends up as a star that does not shine.

We can summarize our theoretical studies by sketching the predicted life history of a star like the sun, as shown in *Figure IV-2*. First, an interstellar cloud somehow starts to collapse. As it heats up by releasing gravitational energy the center may become hot enough so that hydrogen can form helium in a nuclear reaction that produces a great deal more energy. At this point the size, temperature, and brightness of the new star are such that it falls on the main sequence of an H-R diagram. A new star of large mass will fall at the upper left (brighter and hotter); a smaller one falls on the main sequence farther down and to the right (fainter and cooler).

The new star stays at the same brightness and temperature for a long time; that is, it spends most of its life on the main sequence. However, the interior hydrogen is gradually converted to helium, and after billions of years the star begins to change. On the H-R diagram it moves away from the main sequence to the right and up, becoming redder and brighter. The ageing

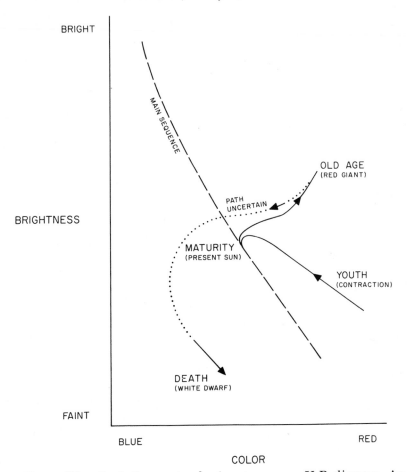

Figure IV-2. Evolutionary track of a star on an H-R diagram. An interstellar gas cloud contracts to form a star which appears first in the lower right of this brightness-color plot. When it reaches the main sequence nuclear fuels begin to burn and the star remains there for a very long time. Eventually it grows brighter and redder, becoming a red giant. After this the predicted path is uncertain, but we do know that a star ends as a white dwarf, plotted in the lower left region.

star gradually evolves into a red giant as its central parts collapse and its outer regions expand. Eventually the gravitational energy released heats the core to a temperature at which nuclear energy can be produced by helium being converted to carbon.

The stages that follow this are not well understood, but heavier chemical elements are probably formed as the star ages. Eventually, perhaps, the star becomes unstable and explodes, leaving behind a white dwarf and blowing off a cloud of gas that enriches the interstellar gas and dust with heavier elements; or perhaps it gradually loses mass by a sort of evaporation before becoming a white dwarf. In any case, debris is left behind out of which new generations of stars can be formed.

This brief account has described the theory of stellar evolution we have today. Obviously there is much more to be done, particularly on the beginning and ending of the life-story of a star. The many possibilities serve to hold the interest of a number of astronomers.

V

Galaxies: Landmarks in the Universe

George O. Abell

The last two chapters have been concerned with individual stars that we see in the sky—how they form from interstellar gas, condense into "adult" stars, shine for a time, and finally "die" as white dwarfs, some of them spewing most of their material back into interstellar space as gas clouds that can form another generation of stars. All this is going on in the vast system of stars, gas, and dust that we call our galaxy.

As explained in Chapter I, this galaxy of ours contains some 100 billion stars, spread out through space in a great wheel so huge that light takes a hundred thousand years or so to go from one side to the other. We see this wheel of stars from our position near the sun, one of the stars inside it, and the rim of the wheel therefore goes right around us. That is, our galaxy appears to us as a concentration of faint, distant stars in the band around the sky we call the Milky Way. This concept of the Milky Way was suggested by Thomas Wright about 1750, and was definitely established by William Herschel in 1787. Until recently it was commonly supposed that our galaxy was essentially the whole universe, and this idea gained strength up to as late as 1920.

As early as 1755, however, there was speculation about other galaxies—other "island universes" outside our own. The famous German philosopher, Immanuel Kant, reasoned that if we could see our galaxy from very far outside, it would appear as a faint, milky, elliptical object. He suggested that elliptical patches of light called "nebulous stars" were other galaxies, but it was not until 168 years later that this identification was firmly established.

Our own galaxy interferes with our view of the outside galaxies. In the denser parts of the Milky Way, such as shown in *Figure I-8,* the stars seem too tightly packed for us to see anything beyond. More than that, there is gas and dust between the stars of our galaxy, and when we look toward the rim of the wheel (horizontally on *Figure I-9*) there is a vast thickness of such obscuring material between us and any outside object. In fact, no outside galaxies are seen in the direction of the rim— that is, near the Milky Way in the sky, as shown in *Figure V-6* (below). But in the other directions (up or down on *Figure I-9*), we are looking through the thin dimension of the dust layer in our own galaxy, and can see outside galaxies unobscured.

The largest and brightest of the outside galaxies that we can see in northern latitudes is shown in *Figure V-1;* it is called the Andromeda Galaxy for the constellation in which it appears, or Messier 31 (M31) because it was the thirty-first object in a list of nebulous patches of light drawn up by the French astronomer Messier in 1784, or NGC 221 because it is No. 221 in the New General Catalog of star clusters and nebulæ, published in 1888. The NGC was a revision of the General Catalog published by Sir John Herschel, son of the great astronomer, William Herschel, whose surveys of the sky, back in the 1780's, established

Figure V-1. The Andromeda Galaxy, Messier 31, a spiral galaxy.
This largest and brightest of the nearby galaxies dwarfs its two companions, M32 on the left and NGC 205 on the right, in this photograph taken with the 48-inch Schmidt telescope. M31 is estimated to
be over 2 million light-years from us. It is the nearest spiral
galaxy, and can just be seen with the naked eye on a clear, dark
night.   *Mount Wilson and Palomar Observatories*

the shape of our own galaxy and discovered thousands of "nebulae"—most of them outside galaxies, but some of them condensations of interstellar gas in our galaxy.

In large modern telescopes the outside galaxies, like M31 in *Figure V-1*, can be seen clearly as wheel-shaped systems of stars, glowing gas clouds, and dark dust clouds. These pictures show, in addition, stars of our own galaxy scattered over the foreground between us and the outside galaxy like drops of rain on a window between us and a distant view. It is evident from such a modern photograph that the outside galaxy is much farther from us than the foreground stars, but the visual observations up to 1880 and the early photographs from 1880 to 1920 were much less clear. So you can understand how it was that many astronomers, as late as 1920, mistook these "spiral nebulae" for relatively small things belonging to our Milky Way system.

The Vast Distances of the Galaxies

How can we measure the distance to a galaxy? It is far too distant for the triangulation methods described in Chapter I. Even the enormous speeds of rotation of a galaxy—200 miles per second, or 6 billion miles per year—are not large enough to show as a displacement in *Figure V-1*, even in 100 years. But we can get an idea of the distance to M31 from the faintness of its individual stars compared to the foreground stars that are perhaps 100 light-years from us (but still within our Milky Way system). The stars in M31 are a million times fainter, and *if they are the same kind of stars* as the foreground stars they would be a thousand times farther away, or 100,000 light-years from us. (This follows because, in clear space, the apparent brightness of a light source decreases with the square of its distance. That is, if a star were 10 times farther away than its actual distance, it would appear 100 times fainter.)

In Chapter III it was shown that some stars are very much more luminous than the average. When we look at a galaxy like M31, the few stars we can pick out are the supergiants—the stars up to hundreds of thousands of times as luminous as our sun. So the comparison with a faint nearby star is unfair; if we want to measure distance by the comparison of brightness, we must pick stars in both M31 and in our own galaxy that have the *same* intrinsic luminosity. We could do this if we had detailed spectra of the stars, but the stars in M31 are so faint that their individual spectra are impossible to photograph with present-day techniques. The first reliable method of measuring the distance to an outside galaxy was based on the apparent faintness of *variable* stars that pulsate in the same manner as nearby variable stars and are therefore likely to be of the same size and luminosity.

These variable stars were discussed briefly in Chapter IV as a peculiar group of stars, probably passing through a brief stage in their evolution. Here we use them as calibrated beacons for measuring distance. The type of variable star called a "Cepheid variable" (because a typical one is in the constellation Cepheus) pulsates regularly from a minimum brightness to about three times brighter in a period of a week or so. There are many of these pulsating stars in two large clouds of stars in the southern sky called the Clouds of Magellan (*Figure V-2*) after the famous circumnavigator. About 1920, Harlow Shapley and other astronomers at the Harvard and Mount Wilson Observatories studied the Cepheid variables in the Magellanic Clouds and elsewhere, and discovered that the average luminosity of such a star depends upon its period of pulsation—the brighter the star, the slower it pulsates. This is to be expected from the mass-luminosity relation (Chapter III) and from the fact that a more massive sphere of gas would pulsate more slowly than a less massive sphere of gas, just as a larger tuning fork vibrates more

Figure V-2. The Large Magellanic Cloud, an irregular galaxy. This
is one of two such clouds easily visible in the southern hemisphere,
but never above the horizon for us in the United States. These two
clouds of Magellan are the nearest known galaxies outside our own.
Mount Wilson and Palomar Observatories

slowly than a smaller one, giving a lower frequency, or pitch.

The period of pulsation of a Cepheid can, therefore, tell us
its true size and luminosity. For instance, if its period is 10 days,

the star is about 5,000 times the luminosity of the sun. First Edwin Hubble and later Walter Baade and others used the large telescopes of the Mount Wilson and Palomar Observatories to measure the apparent brightnesses of variable stars (and other individual stars such as novae) in the outside galaxies, and we now know that the distances to the 30-odd nearest ones are several million light-years.

In the more distant galaxies it is not possible, even with the 200-inch telescope, to see individual stars; the distances to these systems can only be estimated from their total apparent brightnesses—a typical galaxy gives out as much light as about a billion suns. But there are large differences between individual galaxies—a good deal more than between individual people, for example. This can be seen on *Figure V-1,* where the two smaller and fainter patches near M31 are two other galaxies (M32 and NGC 205) at about the same distance from us. M31 is a giant galaxy, at least 60 times brighter than its companions. Moreover, the companions have a different structure.

Types of Galaxies

This leads us to the various types of galaxies observed. It is perhaps remarkable that the thousands of galaxies of reasonable size that have been photographed can be classified in just a few categories, as Hubble first did in the early 1920's. *Figure V-3* and *Figure V-4* show Hubble's types: a sequence of spirals, a sequence of "barred spirals," a sequence of "ellipticals," and the "irregulars." Each sequence is shown by photographs of a few samples; there is a continuous gradation of normal spirals, for example, from the tight-wound "Sa" class to the loose-wound "Sc" class.

In this classification, Hubble recognized that we may see a

Sa NGC 4594

SBa NGC 2859

Sb NGC 2841

SBb NGC 5850

NGC 5457(M 101)

SBc NGC 7479

spiral at any angle to our line of sight: nearly edge-on as in *Figure I-11,* or nearly square-on as in *Figure I-10.* In the case of the ellipticals it is not obvious in advance whether the sequence from E0 to E7 goes from globular galaxies to flattened ones, or whether they are all flattened disks seen at different angles. Statistics, however, show that there are more E0's than expected from chance views of disks, so we presume that there are globular galaxies, but we cannot tell whether any particular E0 is globular, or a disk seen square-on.

Since Hubble first proposed his scheme of classification, other classes have been added, and many differences have been discovered between the classes shown here, some of which are discussed in Chapter VII. One additional class that is now generally accepted is called "So," and fits between the E7 class and the Sa or SBa classes—an intermediate type. Another recently recognized class consists of very faint, very loosely packed elliptical systems that can only be photographed if they are close to us. These are called "Sculptor-type systems" after the constellation where the most famous of them is seen.

The various morphological types—that is, galaxies of different shapes—show definite differences in other characteristics, too. For example, the spirals are bluer than the ellipticals and have more gas clouds in them. It would be very helpful if we could say that all the galaxies of one type have the same intrinsic luminosity. Unfortunately this is not the case, as was found by studying clusters of galaxies such as the one shown in *Figure V-8*

Figure V-3. Types of spiral galaxies. Edwin Hubble, working with the large telescopes at the Mount Wilson Observatory, photographed many galaxies during the 1920's. He was able to classify them as normal spirals, barred spirals, elliptical galaxies, or irregular galaxies. The first two of these classes, as shown here, were further subdivided according to how tightly wound they are. *Yerkes Observatory*

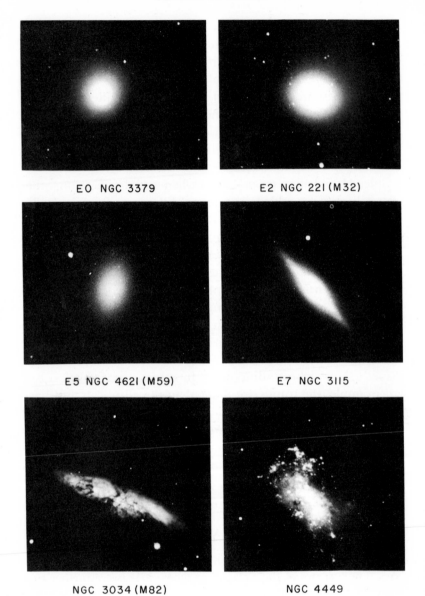

EO NGC 3379

E2 NGC 221(M32)

E5 NGC 4621(M59)

E7 NGC 3115

NGC 3034(M82)

NGC 4449

(below). In such a cluster there is a large number of different types of galaxies at the same distance from us. It is clear that spirals and ellipticals come in all sizes and luminosities, some of them as much as 10,000 times as bright as others in the same class.

However, it is possible nevertheless to estimate relative distances to the clusters of galaxies. This is because the brightest galaxies in all rich clusters are likely to be of about the same luminosity. They are the giant galaxies, more than 10 billion times as luminous as the sun. We can count on every rich cluster's having a few such giants, whereas any one galaxy may be as faint as a million suns, or as bright as 10 billion suns.

Masses of the Galaxies

It has been mentioned several times that our galaxy has about 100 billion stars and you may have wondered where that number came from. It would be remarkable indeed for anyone to count that many! And, in any case, we cannot see all the stars in the Milky Way system because of the obscuring dust between them. How, then, do we know that our galaxy has so many stars?

As mentioned in Chapter I, our galaxy (and any other) would collapse under its own gravitation if it were not rotating. This rotation can be measured, and we find that our sun, at about

---

Figure V-4. Types of elliptical and irregular galaxies. Hubble's class of ellipticals was subdivided according to how nearly circular they are on the photograph, as shown here. The E0 (E-zero) type may be spherical objects, or disks viewed square-on. However, since no elliptical galaxies are observed thinner than the E7 type, these must be in edge-on view. E7 galaxies are thicker than spirals (see *Figure I-11*). *Yerkes Observatory*

30,000 light-years from the center of the galaxy, is moving at about 200 miles per second around it. Now if the galaxy were more massive, the sun would have to go faster to stay in its nearly circular orbit about the center. Thus we can calculate the mass of the galaxy from the rotation of its outermost parts, and it turns out to be about 200 billion times the mass of the sun—"200 billion suns"—of which most is in the form of stars, and the rest interstellar gas and dust.

The same method can be applied to nearby galaxies, such as M31 shown in *Figure V-1*. By the Doppler shift (Chapter II) we find that the stars, gas, and dust on one side of the center of M31 are coming toward us faster than those on the other side. Taking account of the tilt of M31, and knowing the distance from its center to its edge, we find its mass also to be about 200 billion suns. However, several other of the nearby galaxies are found by this method to be much less massive—down to one billion suns—which shows that galaxies vary considerably in amount of material.

Another method of measuring the masses of galaxies is very similar to the one described in Chapter III for determining the masses of stars. It is possible because galaxies often occur in pairs, like the pair shown in *Figure V-5*. These two would fall into each other if they were not revolving about each other, and the speed of this orbital motion (together with the separation of the two) is again a measure of the mass. The major difference between mass determinations for double stars and those for double galaxies is this: the stars take from a few days to a few hundred years to go around each other, whereas the galaxies take, typically, a few hundred million years. Since no one wants to wait that long, we have to be content with Doppler-shift measurements that refer to only a part of the full orbital speed; what part depends upon the unknown angle of the motion to our line of sight. However, the average of such motions in a few

Figure V-5. A close pair of galaxies. Hundreds of close pairs like this have been photographed. The two galaxies must be whirling around one another, otherwise their gravitational attraction would pull them together. From measures of the difference in Doppler shift between spectra of the two galaxies in many pairs, the average mass of one galaxy has been estimated at about 100 billion suns.

Yerkes Observatory

dozen pairs gives a fairly reliable average mass of a galaxy. The results agree reasonably well with the far fewer masses measured by internal rotations. Moreover, as shown recently by Page, the brighter ellipticals are 50 or 60 times more massive than typical spirals and irregulars, on the average.

A third method of measuring masses of galaxies depends on the clusters of galaxies and the assumption that these clusters are stable, lasting features of the universe. If they are to last, the clusters cannot be losing galaxies; that is, most galaxies in a cluster cannot be moving so fast that they will "escape" from the gravitational pull of the whole cluster (as a space probe, for

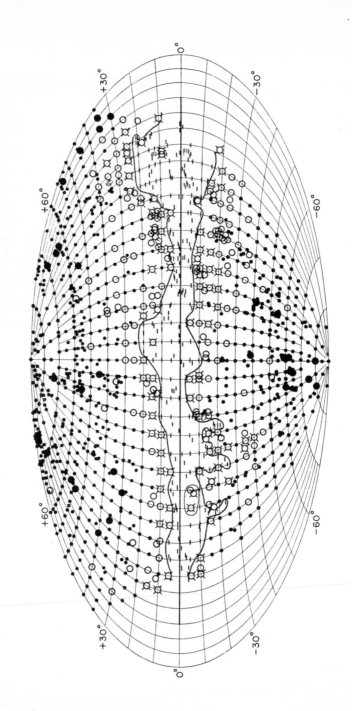

instance, escapes from the earth if it is moving away faster than 7 miles per second). Inverting this argument, we measure by Doppler shifts the speeds of galaxies in a cluster, and calculate the mass of the whole cluster necessary to "hold on to" the fastest moving member galaxies. This total cluster mass is then divided by the total number of galaxies in the cluster to get the average mass of one galaxy.

But here we find a discrepancy: the average mass of a galaxy found from motions in clusters comes out from 10 to 100 times larger than that found by other methods. Since several different observers have obtained similar results on several different clusters, the discrepancy is not likely to be due to an observational error, and two possible explanations have been offered:

(a) There may be material *between* the galaxies—a material like interstellar gas, or burned-out stars—which we cannot see, but which comprises up to 99 per cent of the material in space. (Many astronomers do not like this explanation because it implies that the stars and galaxies we are studying are an insignificant 1 per cent of the material of the universe!)

(b) The clusters of galaxies may slowly be breaking up. But if so, how can there be any clusters left?

A very similar situation exists inside our Milky Way system, where clusters of young, hot, blue stars are found to be breaking up. But in our galaxy new clusters of stars are being formed out of large interstellar gas clouds to keep up the population of star

---

Figure V-6. Distribution of galaxies over the sky. The size of each dot plotted on this map of the sky indicates how many galaxies were counted on a photograph taken with the 100-inch telescope there. Dashes and open circles indicate few or no galaxies, and the irregular region across the center of the map where almost no galaxies are to be seen was called by Hubble the "zone of avoidance." This zone coincides with the visible Milky Way, where interstellar dust obscures the outside galaxies (Chapter I).

clusters. If new clusters of galaxies are to be formed from inter-galactic clouds of material, by analogy, then we are back to the same impasse as in (a), and the majority of material in the universe is between the galaxies, as yet unobserved. This riddle of the clusters of galaxies is a question that excites astronomers today.

Distribution of the Galaxies in Space

So far in this chapter we have considered the galaxies as individuals, and discussed their shapes, distances, masses, and motions. Now we turn to their distribution—the whole picture of the universe as provided by our view of the galaxies.

Figure V-6 shows a plot made by Hubble of the density of galaxies found on actual photographs in various parts of the sky. The plot shows a gap along the Milky Way that we explained earlier as due to the obscuring clouds of dust near us in our own galaxy. There are also some irregularities due to the larger clusters. But by-and-large the galaxies Hubble photographed in half-hour exposures with the 100-inch telescope are distributed uniformly over the unobscured part of the sky. (We assume that they would be uniform over the obscured region if we could get outside our own galaxy for a look.)

Moreover, if we look farther out in space, by using a larger telescope, or longer exposure photographs, we see more galaxies in approximately the proportion expected for uniform density. That is, if we look twice as far we see about eight times as many. (A sphere of twice the radius has eight times the volume.) We are not sure that this relation is exact for galaxies at the furthest limit of our largest telescopes, however, because it is difficult to measure brightnesses of faint galaxies accurately enough to tell.

As a first approximation, at least, the galaxies are spread

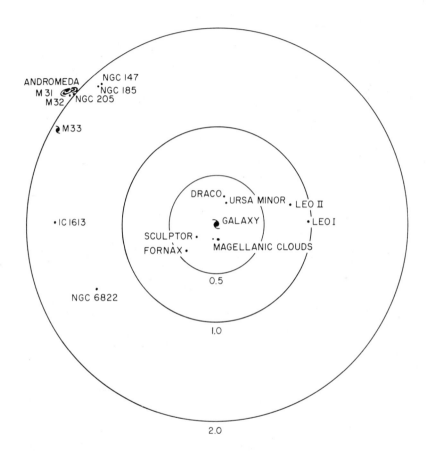

Figure V-7. The Local Group of galaxies. The positions of the nearest known galaxies are plotted here on an arbitrary plane. They are corrected for their outward motion (away from our galaxy) during the time since the light we see started toward us. The sizes of the galaxies are shown roughly to scale; this diagram represents, therefore, a distant view of the Local Group. The circles centered on our own galaxy indicate distances in millions of light-years. (The distances are known only approximately and may be revised by future research.)

uniformly through space to distances of 2 or 3 billion light-years on every side—and there probably are more beyond that. But when we look more carefully, and plot their positions in detail, we find close pairs, groups, and large clusters of galaxies, as already mentioned. Our own Milky Way Galaxy is in a "local group" of 17 galaxies somewhat closer together than average, as plotted in *Figure V-7*. And within the local group there are two close triples; the Magellanic Clouds (*Figure V-2*) are two irregular galaxies separated from our Milky Way Galaxy by a distance comparable to its diameter, and M31, M32, and NGC 205 form another close triple (*Figure V-1*).

Somewhat farther afield we come to larger groupings like the one shown in *Figure V-8*—a cluster of at least 2,000 galaxies. There are other clusters of 10,000 galaxies and more, and these clusters of galaxies, like the galaxies themselves, seem to be spread throughout space as far as we can see. Moreover, as *Figure V-9* shows, the clusters themselves seem to cluster, and we may yet find clustering of these clusters of clusters. This hierarchy of clusters may have an important bearing on theories of cosmology because it does not imply an infinite gravitational force from all sides on every bit of mass, as would be calculated with Newton's Law of Gravitation for an infinite, uniform universe.

Figure V-8. A great cluster of galaxies in the constellation Corona Borealis. This cluster, photographed with the 200-inch telescope, is probably a billion light-years from us. Most of the irregular specks on the photograph are galaxies in the cluster; the sharp round images are foreground stars. The total number of galaxies in the cluster may exceed ten thousand, and there are hundreds of such clusters known. *Mount Wilson and Palomar Observatories*

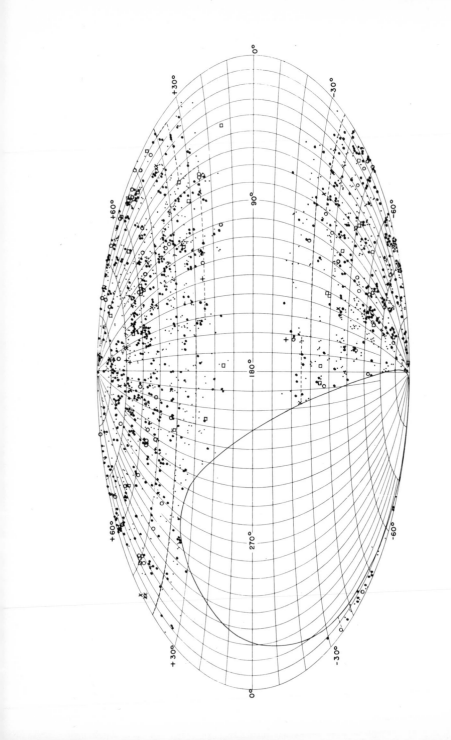

The Law of Redshifts

One of the most remarkable facts about the galaxies was discovered by Hubble and Humason in 1929 and is illustrated in *Figure V-10*. The farther a galaxy is from us, the more rapidly it seems to be receding from us, as shown by the shift of its spectrum toward the red. Some people have doubted the reality of this speed of recession and have postulated some new and special effect on light moving great distances through space. Undoubtedly they find it hard to believe that galaxies can be moving so fast—tens of thousands of miles per second. But the astronomers who work with these spectra have no reason to believe that the familiar Doppler shift somehow changes into something else at greater distances. The Doppler shift as an effect of speed is well confirmed by laboratory experiments, by observations in the solar system, and by observations of double stars. In these cases we can see the light sources, planets or stars, actually moving.

There is no obvious reason, then, to think that the larger shifts in *Figure V-10* are due to a different cause. Nevertheless, some scientists stress the fact that the observed redshifts could be largely due to a different cause such as "the tiring of light as it moves through space." If this were the case, of course, it would be necessary to subtract part of the total measured redshifts in

---

Figure V-9. Distribution of the rich clusters of galaxies over the sky. Each symbol represents a cluster of many galaxies; the larger the symbol, the closer the cluster. The most distant are probably about 2 billion light-years away. The empty region along the middle of the diagram is the zone of avoidance in the Milky Way, as in *Figure V-6*. The large, oval, empty region on the left is the part of the sky too far south to be surveyed from Palomar Mountain where the study of clusters was carried out by the author.

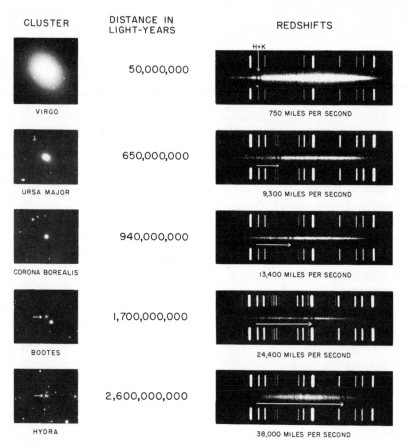

CLUSTER	DISTANCE IN LIGHT-YEARS	REDSHIFTS
VIRGO	50,000,000	750 MILES PER SECOND
URSA MAJOR	650,000,000	9,300 MILES PER SECOND
CORONA BOREALIS	940,000,000	13,400 MILES PER SECOND
BOOTES	1,700,000,000	24,400 MILES PER SECOND
HYDRA	2,600,000,000	38,000 MILES PER SECOND

Figure V-10. Relation between redshift and distance. On the left are photographs of individual galaxies in successively more distant clusters; on the right their spectra, showing the Doppler shift of two strong absorption lines due to ionized calcium. The distances are estimated from the faintness of galaxies in each cluster.

Mount Wilson and Palomar Observatories

order to get Doppler shifts due to true motion. According to how large such an effect is assumed to be, the true motions of galaxies might have almost any value. Until such an unknown effect is shown to exist, however, most astronomers accept the measured redshifts of galaxies as Doppler shifts. That is, they accept the Law of Redshifts as meaning that outside galaxies are generally moving away from our galaxy with speeds proportional to their distances. In addition, of course, there are small random motions superimposed on this general recession. For example, the motion of one galaxy around another in a pair, and the individual motions of galaxies in clusters, are added to (or subtracted from) the general recession of *Figure V-10*.

There is an immediate and important inference from the Law of Redshifts: since the velocity is defined as distance moved in unit time, and since Hubble found the velocities of galaxies proportional to their distances, the galaxies we now observe must have all been much closer together billions of years ago. For example, a galaxy at a distance of 100 million light-years is going away from us at 1,400 miles per second or 0.008 light-years per year, so it took about 13 billion years to go from near us to where it is now.* A galaxy twice as far away is going twice as fast, so it, too, has taken 13 billion years to get there. In other words, if we trace their motions back in time (assuming constant speeds), we find that all galaxies started with different outward speeds from near us about 13 billion years ago, and the faster moving ones have just been able to get farther away.

* These numbers have been changed over the past 10 years due to corrections in the distance scale. The figures quoted here are based upon the best modern measurements, but are still very provisional.

Light Travel-Time

One little confusion arises here: the distant galaxies are really even farther away than they seem. Remember that a galaxy at a billion light-years' distance appears to us now as it was a billion years ago, since the light took that long to reach us. And during that light travel-time, the galaxy has been moving at 14,000 miles per second—0.08 light-years per year—and is now about 1.1 billion light-years away. This is just one of the corrections that must be applied to the measurements. The redshift itself weakens a galaxy's light—the very light, or brightness, that we are using to estimate distance. However, these corrections are small for galaxies and clusters up to medium distances. Therefore the Hubble Law of Redshifts shows that velocity of recession is quite accurately proportional to distance out to 2 billion light-years or more, and it is only for the most distant galaxies that there may be a deviation.

You may think that, because all the galaxies are receding from us, our galaxy is at the center of the universe. Such a conclusion would be contrary to the idea developed in Chapter I, and dignified with the name "Cosmological Principle," that our position in the universe cannot be a special one. As a matter of fact, the Hubble Law makes our position no different from that of any other galaxy. You can see this by considering four galaxies, *A, B, C,* and *D,* in a line from left to right at equal spacing of 100 million light-years, as shown in *Figure V-11.* Suppose we are on galaxy *B;* then, according to Hubble's Law, we see *A* moving at 1,400 miles per second to the left, *C* moving at 1,400 mi/sec to the right, and *D* moving at 2,800 mi/sec to the right.

Now consider what an observer on *C* sees. On the right, *D* is moving away from him at 1,400 mi/sec; on the left, *B* is moving away from him at 1,400 mi/sec, and *A* at 2,800 mi/sec. In

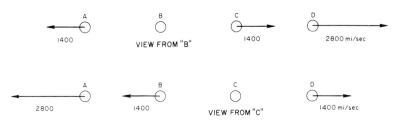

Figure V-11. The expanding universe has no center. The Hubble Law of Redshifts implies that observers in the galaxies *A, B, C,* and *D* will each see all the rest moving away from him. Hence, we cannot conclude from the recession of galaxies on all sides of us that we are at the center.

other words, this observer on another galaxy also sees all galaxies moving away from him at speeds proportional to distance. The Hubble Law is such that an observer on any galaxy will see all the others moving away from him as if he were at the "center." But this means that there is no special or preferred position—no one galaxy is any more "at the center" than any other—consistent with the Cosmological Principle.

Cosmology, the Search for Order in the Universe

The foregoing sections have described galaxies very briefly and outlined what is known about their distribution through space and their motions. It is the goal of cosmology to fit all these observations, together with the laws of physics, into one consistent theory that applies to the whole universe—to everything we can see and anything else that may be beyond the view of the largest telescopes. A typical question to be answered by cosmology—a question that has concerned thinking men for centuries—is whether the universe is infinite or limited in some way. So far we have no evidence of any edge, but of course there could be one out beyond our most distant observations. Few students of cosmology expect this, however; a simple edge to the universe would be contrary to the Cosmological Principle. An observer in a galaxy near the edge would get a view of the universe entirely different from ours.

This reasoning illustrates how speculation enters cosmology (as it enters most scientific research). It is a guess or a hunch, for instance, that the Cosmological Principle is valid—that one observer's view of the universe should be essentially the same as any other's. What is more, the cosmologist is working with only part of the facts; the observations of galaxies will probably never be complete, and are now meager indeed compared to all that we now realize we do *not* know.

It is, therefore, not surprising that cosmology has produced more than one answer—that there are several theories of the universe, all of them consistent with observations, but differing widely among themselves. Two of these theories, the "Big-Bang" and "Continuous-Creation" Theories described below, are extremes of a sort, since they lead to almost opposite conclusions. They have both received a good deal of attention recently, and many astronomers are now searching for observations that will support or disprove one or the other. But it should be emphasized that *both* may be wrong; other acceptable theories of cosmology have already been proposed, and still others will undoubtedly be proposed in the future.

In both of the theories to be discussed the observed redshifts in the spectra of galaxies are presumed to be Doppler shifts; that is, we do not assume that there is some other effect producing the redshifts, but that the galaxies are really moving away from us at very high speeds.

Theories of a Changing Universe

The fact that most galaxies are moving away from us (the expansion of the universe) would seem to imply that things are changing—evolving. Several theories, including the one popularly known as the "Big-Bang" Theory, are based on the concept that the universe is evolving. It is reasonable to say that, since the galaxies are all moving away from each other, the average density of matter must be getting smaller as time goes on. That is, the density of galaxies was much greater in the past than it is now.

Although the reasoning of the cosmologists was more complex, we can say that the idea of the Big-Bang Theory comes simply from following the motions of galaxies back to the time when all of them were close together. If their speeds were always the same as those we observe today, this must have been from 10 to 15 billion years ago. In the Big-Bang Theory it is assumed that all the matter of the universe was tightly packed together at this "beginning" and then for some reason started to fly apart in the biggest explosion of all time. The motions would not stay exactly the same from then till now, since gravitational attraction would have slowed down the explosion fragments, particularly when they were close together at the start.

One of the first cosmologists to propose this idea (in the early 1920's) was the Abbé Lemaître, a Belgian, who called it a theory of the "Primeval Atom," referring to the original single chunk of matter. Lemaître wished to explain the cosmic rays as a present-day remainder of the initial explosion. More recently a group of American physicists led by George Gamow has used the idea of the "Big Bang" in an attempt to explain how the chemical elements were formed in the relative amounts we observe today. Gamow and his collaborators reasoned what nuclear reactions would go on in all the matter of the universe during the Big Bang. Their idea was that electrons, protons, and neutrons, forming the hot, dense material during the Big Bang, would combine to form hydrogen, helium, and heavier atoms. As the material expanded, the hot gases would cool, large clots would form and later become galaxies, and smaller clots within these would later become stars.

There are difficulties in the calculations of element formation, but otherwise the general scheme of the Big-Bang Theory provides a basis for understanding what we see today: stars grouped in galaxies that are moving away from one another. The start of the explosion some billions of years ago takes on special significance; if all matter was then in the form of electrons, neutrons, and protons at high temperature, we could never expect to discover by observation today what went on before. That is, the beginning of the explosion was a "beginning" in a broader sense, and it can be considered that the universe was created then.

There remains the question of the boundary; if the mass of the universe is not infinite, it would seem that the original exploding matter must have had an edge. Is this a violation of the Cosmological Principle?

General Relativity in Cosmology

Although it may not seem quite "fair" to those of us brought up on Euclid, the unwanted edge of the universe can be eliminated by changing geometry. "Curved space," a common term that is little understood, is possible in new kinds of geometry undreamed of by Euclid. In fact, strange as it seems, in curved space the universe can be finite but unbounded—it can have a volume of only so many cubic miles, but no edge.

As everyone knows, Albert Einstein developed the ideas of relativity in the early 1900's. He introduced the curvature of space as a means of explaining gravitation; that is, he assumed that the curvature is locally greater near a massive body, and that the general curvature depends on the average density of matter. This explains Newton's gravitation, and also some additional small effects that are now accepted as proving Einstein's assumption.*

It is doubtful that anyone can visualize curved space, but it is helpful to think of the similar situation on the curved surface of the earth, where the *area* is finite but unbounded, and the geometry is not exactly Euclidean. (In a very large triangle on the earth's surface, the angles add up to more than two right angles). Also, there is no "center" to the surface area of the earth, just as there is no center to the finite volume of curved space. Moreover, there is a "radius" of curved space that is connected with the whole volume (as the radius of the earth is connected with its whole area) and with the longest distance one can move in a "straight line" before coming back to the starting point.

The major difference between the curved surface of the earth and the curved volume of space in relativistic cosmology is that the space curvature may be changing—*must* be changing, if the density of matter is changing. Einstein and a number of others have worked out ways in which this could happen. One of these ways is the "Big Bang," another is a contracting universe, and

* The three observations supporting Einstein's General Theory of Relativity are: (1) Stars are slightly displaced away from the sun when observed during total solar eclipse, showing that light rays are slightly bent as they pass close by the sun. (2) A fast-moving planet like Mercury does not move exactly as predicted by Newton's laws; over a century the axis of its elliptical orbit shifts 43 seconds of arc more than predicted by Newtonian theory. (3) The light from a very dense star suffers a small redshift (in wavelength) compared with light from a less dense star.

there are also oscillating models in which space curvature grows larger, then smaller.

From what we have observed of the motions of the galaxies away from each other, the contracting model of the universe can be ruled out. But cosmologists are still left with the question, "What has caused the present expansion of the universe?" It is one result of the mathematics of relativistic cosmology that there can be a *repulsion* between distant galaxies that might actually overcome their gravitational attraction. In the equations, this repulsion is represented by a quantity called the "cosmological constant." But, although it is expected mathematically, there is no clear basis for setting the amount of the repulsion. Einstein first picked an amount that would just balance gravitational attraction (before the redshifts of galaxies were generally known). He felt that the universe should be neither exploding nor collapsing. Nowadays, though it is taken for granted that the universe is expanding, most cosmologists assume *no* repulsion (or "cosmological constant zero") and leave the cause of expansion unspecified.

Without repulsion the motions of galaxies after an initial explosion would be slowed down by gravitation in the same way that a rocket space-probe fired away from the earth is slowed down by the earth's gravity. If the rocket is fired at a speed greater than about 7 miles per second (the "escape velocity") it will move away from the earth forever. The galaxies, if they were started fast enough in a "Big Bang," could likewise move outward forever; if they started slower than some "escape velocity" they would fall back together. And the size of the critical "escape velocity" depends upon the size of the "cosmological-constant" repulsion as well as on the average density of matter.

This description shows how complicated relativistic cosmology is, and how many possible "models of the universe" need to be tested by observation. Although progress is being made, we are still far from a definitive test. For example, we do not yet know the average density of matter accurately enough to predict the critical "escape velocity." This, and the other uncertainties, mean that several possible relativistic models of the universe must be kept in mind, the expanding one of the Big-Bang Theory being the simplest. If gravitation has slowed down the motions of galaxies, the age of the universe since the start of the initial explosion would be less than 13 billion years (from the Hubble Law). One of the difficulties with the Big-Bang concept is that some astronomers estimate ages of some star clusters in our galaxy at 15 billion years or more, as was shown in Chapters III and IV.

The "Steady-State" Theory: An Unchanging Universe

The problems of the finite age implied by relativistic cosmology, and of beginnings and endings, have led several British astronomers (Hoyle, Bondi, Gold, and others) to speculate on the possibilities of another cosmological hypothesis. Theirs is perhaps the simplest of the many possible cosmological models because it rests upon a single assumption that is an extension of the Cosmological Principle. This assumption is called the *perfect cosmological principle;* it states that the universe is not only the same *everywhere* (except for local small-scale irregularities), but at *all times.* In other words, if we could return to life billions of years hence, we would find the universe, on the whole, as it is now. Since nothing would change in time, this model is known as the "Steady-State" Cosmology.

By starting with this premise, the English team rules out any creation of the universe at a definite time in the past. Moreover, they must explain how our view of the universe can remain the same when galaxies are moving apart—how the average density of matter can stay constant when galaxies are leaving our region of space at high speeds on all sides. They explain this by the bold assumption that *matter is being created continuously in empty space* at a rate just sufficient to replace what is leaving due to the recession of galaxies observed by Hubble. The theory, therefore, is sometimes called the "Continuous-Creation" Theory. Moreover, to satisfy the perfect cosmological principle, there must always be the same proportion of young and old galaxies in any given volume of space. This condition requires that the creation of new matter be always proportional to the amount of matter present, and that the rate of expansion of the distance between any two galaxies (or clusters of galaxies) be proportional to their current separation. According to this theory, the new matter that comes into being is usually presumed to be in the form of gas (possibly individual atoms of pure hydrogen), which later condenses into galaxies and stars.

It is important to understand that in the Steady-State Cosmology, *individual* galaxies are formed, age, grow old, and, as their stars evolve to the black-dwarf state, finally die. Only when we consider a large volume of space, containing many galaxies, are things unchanging—there will always be young and old galaxies, side by side, and always in the same proportions. The formation of new matter needs to take place only at a very slow rate, and we should not necessarily expect to find newly formed galaxies in our immediate vicinity in space. (It is possible, however, that we do observe young galaxies nearby. See Chapter VII.) The universe itself, according to this theory, is infinitely large and infinitely old—with no beginning and no end.

It is often objected that matter cannot be created spontaneously from nothing. On the other hand, the proponents of the

Steady-State Theory maintain that it is no more difficult to imagine matter being created gradually and steadily than all at once in some "big bang" in the past.

Tests of Cosmological Theories

There are three distinct stages in the progress of scientific research: (1) systematic observing, or the collecting of experimental results; (2) forming hypotheses to account for what was observed; and (3) testing these hypotheses by further observations or experiments. In the realm of cosmology we have described (1) the observations of galaxies, and (2) two hypotheses ("Big-Bang" and "Continuous-Creation") which, without the testing of stage (3), would remain as separate, unproved speculations along with many others.

It is clear that evidence favoring one of these hypotheses over the others will depend upon *differences* between them. Since all of the cosmological models described here refer to a universe expanding at the rate indicated by Hubble's Law of Redshifts, the differences between them must reflect the different ways in which the theories predict the universe will change in time. In other words, for testing cosmological theories we need observations of the universe as it was long ago to compare with present conditions. Fortunately, we can and do look into the past. This is because light travels at a finite speed, so that we see remote objects as they were when the light left them—up to billions of years ago for galaxies at distances of billions of light-years.

One of the possibly observable differences between the Steady-State and the Big-Bang Cosmologies is in the predicted mixture of galaxies of different ages. According to the Steady-State Theory, individual galaxies age and die but new ones are always forming, so that old and young galaxies have always existed side by side. No matter how far out in space we look, therefore, we should not find galaxies, on the average, any different from those near us. The Big-Bang Cosmology, on the other hand, assumes a distinct "beginning," so that all galaxies have about the same age. Thus, if we look out to a great distance, and hence far back in time, we should find galaxies that are systematically younger than those near us—that is, remote galaxies should be at an earlier stage of evolution.

Another test depends on how the average density of matter in space changes in time. Evolutionary cosmologies (e.g., the Big-Bang Theory) require that matter gradually thins out in space; remote galaxies, therefore, should appear relatively closer together (as they were in the past) than nearby ones. The Steady-State Theory, however, predicts that the average distance between galaxies never changes, and so should be the same for galaxies at all distances.

A third, less obvious test involves the speeds of receding galaxies at great distances. The Big-Bang Theory predicts that the rate of expansion of the universe should change in time; how it should change depends upon the amount of repulsion assumed (the value of the "cosmological constant"). For no repulsion (cosmological constant zero), the expansion should slow down, because of the gravitational forces between galaxies. In the Steady-State Theory, on the other hand, the rate of the separation of any two galaxies is ever increasing. That is, these two cosmological theories predict different relations between redshift and distance for the remote galaxies.

Unfortunately, very accurate observations are required to confirm one of the cosmological models by any of these tests; at present, astronomers are on the verge of making sufficiently critical observations, but have not yet succeeded with certainty. It is very difficult to measure systematic differences that might be due to these evolutionary effects, because the galaxies that we see as they were billions of years ago are very distant and therefore very faint. For those faint, very distant galaxies, it is not yet possible to measure distances accurately enough to tell whether the density of the universe is changing in time. It is possible, however, that some of the extragalactic radio sources may be remote galaxies or clusters of galaxies (see Chapter VI). There is some hope that counts of the numbers of weak cosmic radio sources may confirm or disprove one or the other cosmological theory.

Of the three tests, the most promising at present is probably the third. The two theories predict different velocities of galaxies at large distances from us, and these predictions can be compared with the observed velocities. Redshifts have now been measured for galaxies moving away from us at speeds of over 40 per cent of the speed of light. But there is as yet no reliable procedure for measuring accurately the relative distances of these remote objects. When one is developed, we shall be able to determine whether the rate of expansion of the universe is increasing or decreasing—that is, which theory matches the observations.

We should not expect, however, that one or the other of the cosmological theories we have described will turn out to be "correct." Both theories are based upon highly simplifying assumptions. Our ideas in the realm of cosmology may be as rudimentary as those of the Greek philosophers 2,500 years ago, who believed that all "heavenly" motions must occur in perfect circles. It would be very surprising if, after the next century, scientists have finally settled upon one or the other of the specific theories we have described above. There is an excellent chance, on the other hand, that in the next decade or so we shall be able to eliminate from the realm of possibility one or both of these models. In popular writings, we often read that certain astronomers "believe" a particular cosmological theory, but the implication is misleading. Hoyle and Bondi, for example, do not necessarily *believe* in the Steady-State Theory—it is only a hypothesis, an idea, that they have suggested to "try out." In science we are always trying out ideas—hypotheses; while they "work," we accept them. As soon as they fail to describe observed phenomena, we are equally quick to discard them in favor of better representations of nature.

VI

Radio Broadcasts from the Depths of Space

Ronald N. Bracewell

A branch of astronomy that has recently opened up enables us to get a new view of the universe using the radio waves coming to the earth from the outside instead of the light waves. Why should radio waves be coming to the earth? It has been reasonable to expect that they would, ever since the 1890's, when the theory of radiation was first worked out by physicists. This theory showed that hot bodies emit electromagnetic waves of all wavelengths, not merely heat and light. Earlier it had been shown that radio waves, like light waves, are electromagnetic. The two differ only in wavelength. Consequently, it was reasonable to assume that an object like the sun, very hot and not too far away, and known to be giving out light and heat, must also be giving out radio waves.

An attempt was made just before 1900 to pick up such radio waves from the sun, but at that time radio receivers were not sensitive enough. Some years later, when better amplifiers could be built, the idea had been lost, and it was not until the 1930's that the first radio waves from outside were detected by Jansky, and later by Grote Reber, both in the United States. These radio waves do not have the organized character of waves from a radio-broadcasting station; in their random nature they are more like heat radiation from the sun. If you could make them audible and listen to them in your radio receiver you would simply hear "static," or noise.

The Radio View of the Universe

Not only the sun, but a number of other things that give out radio noise were found in the sky; the Milky Way is responsible for a good deal, and also a number of point sources called "radio stars." Many hundreds of the latter were found, and it looked more or less as though observation of radio waves would produce results similar to those pieced together from looking at the sky through an optical telescope. However, it was soon discovered that many of the "brightest" radio stars are not in the same positions in the sky as any visible stars and so must be a different kind of thing. In particular, when one turned a powerful optical telescope toward the two strongest of these radio stars, known as Cygnus A and Cassiopeia A (because of the constellations in which they are located), nothing at all was to be seen.

This raises a philosophical question. A book that was written before 1930 would describe the universe in terms of its visible contents, and would assume that there is little that is invisible. In order to understand the new radio observations, however, it seems necessary to assume the presence of a great deal in the universe that is invisible, and the question is—what does the universe really consist of? Is it what we see, or is it something more complex?

As a further example, when we look at the sun with a radio antenna tuned to 10-cm waves, we find that it is about 10 per cent larger than what we see or photograph. Which is correct? This makes you realize that it is simply an accident of evolution that our eyes are sensitive to visible light. If men had evolved with radio antennas instead of eyes, we would have said that the sun was 10 per cent larger. So our description of the universe really depends on the form to which man has evolved—with eyes that see light; if we use a different kind of observing instrument, the universe can look different.

The real interest of the new radio astronomy is that it enables us to get new information about things that are invisible or transparent in visible light, so that we now have a fuller picture of the universe than we did before. In Chapter V you have seen some optical pictures of galaxies resembling our own galaxy. There are no such pictures of our own Milky Way Galaxy because no photographer has been sufficiently far away to get it into his field of view, but it is inferred that our galaxy has a spiral structure. It contains about a hundred billion stars distributed in a flat pancake with a central condensation.

A Radio Map of Our Milky Way Galaxy

All the spiral galaxies are surprisingly flat things; their thickness is only about one per cent of their diameter. Now a galaxy is extremely large; why should it be so flat? What keeps the stars out near the edge, 30 or 40 thousand light-years away from the ones near the center, in that flat plane? The stars themselves are very far apart from one another, and we know of no particular influence that would cause stars to be concentrated in the same plane with other stars. This is one of the key problems in the development and life-history of a galaxy treated in

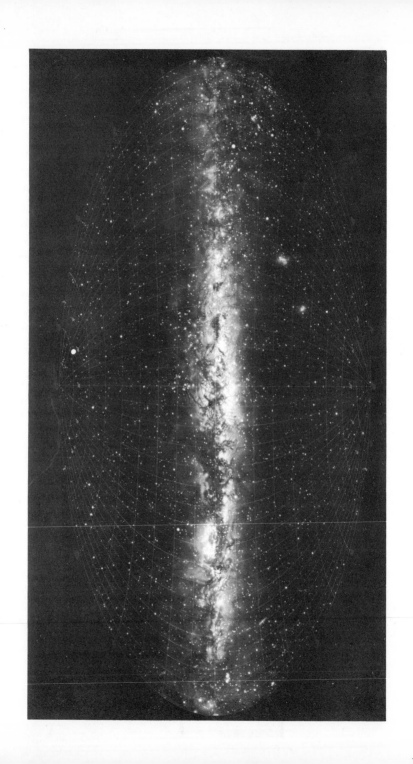

Chapter VII in more detail. In order to solve a problem like this we need all the facts we can get; we should not limit ourselves to photographs taken with light.

Figure VI-1 is the best picture of our own galaxy we can get by optical means. It was painted by an artist as a composite of photographs of the Milky Way all the way around the sky, and shows how the stars are concentrated toward an equatorial plane. Because this is a picture as seen from the earth, it does not show the extreme flattening mentioned above. What we see here are mainly stars near us in space. The great majority of the stars in the galaxy are invisible for a reason that is quite clear: along the equatorial plane is a layer of "smog"—dark areas running more or less along the center line—that obscures the light from distant stars. If that smog were not there and we could see to the edge of the galaxy, then we would see a much more extreme concentration of faint stars.

Figure VI-2 shows a radio survey of part of the same region of the sky—a map on which the contours represent the intensity of radio emission from each part of the sky. The most intense concentration is in the direction toward the center of the galaxy, and the radio emission fades away toward both ends of the map in a somewhat irregular way. We know that these radio waves can penetrate the interstellar smog; the minute particles of solid material that impede the passage of light do not affect radio waves because the wavelength is so much larger than the

---

Figure VI-1. A composite drawing of the Milky Way. Put together from many photographs of the sky, this picture gives as clear an impression as possible by optical means of our Milky Way Galaxy seen from near one edge. Interstellar dust—"smog" that shows in places as dark clouds—prevents our seeing across the galaxy. Nevertheless, the faint (distant) stars are strongly concentrated toward the central line—toward a single plane in space. *Lund Observatory*

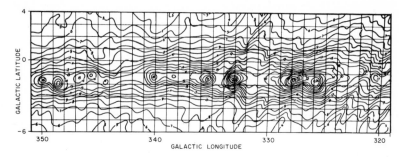

Figure VI-2. Radio contour map of part of the Milky Way. Each contour line is drawn through points from which the measured radio intensity is the same. The area shown is about one tenth the width and height of *Figure VI-1* at the center of that figure. The highest radio intensity is seen to come from the center of our Milky Way Galaxy. However, radio emission is *not* as concentrated as the faint stars.   *B. Y. Mills*

diameter of the smog particles. Consequently, the radio telescope sees right through to the edge of the galaxy, and we see the strong concentration in the direction of the center of the galaxy. However, we do not see so strong a concentration as we would expect along the rest of the Milky Way. *Figure VI-2* shows that the galactic belt of radio radiation is many degrees wide; that is, the system of radio emitters is not particularly flattened. Calculations show that the radio emission is *not* coming from the same volume of space that is occupied by the stars; some of it is, but the bulk of it is coming from a larger, more spherical volume in which the galaxy of stars is imbedded. The radio telescope shows, then, that our galaxy is imbedded in a spherical volume of something that is emitting radio waves very strongly.

Radio Emission by Hydrogen Atoms

The kind of radio noise discussed so far consists of many different radio wavelengths. We usually detect just one band of wavelengths at a time, by tuning the radio receiver; but we find the other wavelengths there, too. Because many wavelengths are present, this radio noise is analogous to the white light (continuous spectra) of stars mentioned in Chapter II. There is also another kind of cosmic radio emission that corresponds to the bright lines in optical spectra. The only source of such radio waves observable at present is cold hydrogen in atomic form. Atoms of cold hydrogen emit radio waves that are very precisely of a single wavelength, 21 centimeters or about $8\frac{1}{3}$ inches (a frequency of 1420 megacycles).

A radio-telescope receiver tuned to this wavelength gives a picture of the sky very different from *Figure VI-2*. It shows all the cold, atomic hydrogen; not the high-temperature hydrogen in the atmospheres of stars, but the very low-density, cold hydrogen atoms between the stars—the interstellar gas clouds. Moreover, the precise wavelength received will be changed by the Doppler shift if the emitting hydrogen is moving toward us or away from us. This change in wavelength can be measured, and from it, the currents in the interstellar gas calculated.

A radio telescope that can be accurately tuned to a frequency on either side of 1420 megacycles is therefore a powerful instrument for exploring the interstellar gas in the Milky Way. This has been carried out by the Dutch astronomers at Leiden who, in conjunction with the Australians, have been able to trace the moving spiral arms of our galaxy. The concentration of the interstellar hydrogen gas is found to be extreme; it forms a thin flat sheet through the equatorial plane of the galaxy—a thin line down the middle of *Figure VI-2*. In fact, this sheet of hydrogen gas is so flat that it is now used as the reference plane in the galaxy—the plane from which astronomers measure positions.

The 21-centimeter radio observations also show how much hydrogen gas is present, both in our own galaxy and in outside galaxies. Such measurements confirm the difference in gas content between the irregular, spiral, and elliptical types of galaxies described in Chapter V.

Optical Identification of Radio Stars

There are many forms of radio telescopes. *Figure VI-3* shows an instrument at Stanford University which is notable for its unsurpassed resolving power; its beamwidth is only 3 × 3 minutes of arc. Many radio stars reveal internal structure when observed with this instrument, which is a delicately adjusted

Figure VI-3. The Stanford University radio telescope. In general, the larger the aperture of a telescope, the greater its resolving power (Chapter II). However, this radio telescope achieves very high resolving power by combining the radio signals received from several small dish-antennas. It can distinguish two radio stars as close as 1.5 minutes of arc. *Stanford University*

combination of 10-foot-diameter paraboloidal reflectors. It is also able to determine the location of radio stars in the sky with fairly high precision.

As already mentioned, the two strongest radio stars for some time defied attempts to identify them with optical objects; in *Figure VI-4* we see a photograph of the very first optical object to be identified with a radio star. It is the Crab Nebula, a fantastic thing that first achieved fame as a new optical star in 1054 A.D., as has been mentioned in Chapter III. Government records kept in China at that time report that a new star of tremendous brightness appeared in the sky at this position. What we see now is not the star itself but a mass of gas fired out from the old explosion and still moving outward. The star that blew up—a supernova—has now subsided into an optically inconspicuous object, but this mass of gas still gives out very intense radio waves.

The Crab Nebula provided data for the first break-through in understanding radio stars; it was suggested first by the Soviet astrophysicist Shklovsky that high velocity electrons are speeding around in this object, accelerated in a magnetic field that he assumed was also there. Since it is well known from theory and laboratory experiments in physics that such acceleration causes electrons to emit radio waves, this was a reasonable explanation. Better yet, a test could be applied to Shklovsky's theory; if high-speed electrons are moving in a magnetic field, they would also emit polarized light, something that is unusual and easily detected. Indeed, when optical measures were made, they proved that the Crab Nebula *is* emitting highly polarized light, thus giving very strong support to Shklovsky's hypothesis of high-speed electrons in a magnetic field. This proved to be a clue that helped us to understand several other radio stars also.

A radio source known as Virgo A (the brightest radio star in

Figure VI-4. The Crab Nebula, a radio source in our galaxy. The first optical object identified with a radio star, this cloud of glowing gas undoubtedly resulted from a supernova explosion in 1054 A.D. Light from this nebula is found to be polarized, confirming the theory that there is a magnetic field causing free electrons in the gas to broadcast radio waves.   *Mount Wilson and Palomar Observatories*

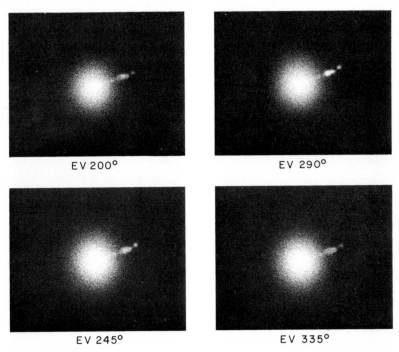

EV 200°   EV 290°

EV 245°   EV 335°

Figure VI-5. Polarization of light from the galaxy M87, radio star Virgo A. The four photographs were made with a polaroid filter at different angles. Differences in the brightness of the jet on the upper right of M87 show that its light is polarized, thus confirming the theory that magnetic fields in the jet from this elliptical galaxy are responsible for radio emission.

Mount Wilson and Palomar Observatories

the constellation Virgo) is shown in four optical pictures in *Figure VI-5*. Referring to *Figure V-4*, you can see that this is an elliptical galaxy, a type of galaxy that has no spiral structure. However, this particular elliptical galaxy has a unique feature —a jet protrudes from it. It was immediately suggested that the jet might be responsible for the strong radio emission, in which case it should also emit polarized light. The four photographs in *Figure VI-5* were taken with a polarization analyzer in four different directions, and reveal that the light is indeed polarized (since the jet is of different brightness in each photograph).

Another quite different radio star, Centaurus A, is located in the southern sky, not readily observable from the United States. An optical photograph (*Figure VI-6*) shows that it is another peculiar elliptical galaxy, this one crossed by a strong smog belt, which is very unusual for an elliptical galaxy. In fact, some astronomers think that *Figure VI-6* shows *two* galaxies: an ordinary elliptical in the background, and an ordinary spiral seen edge-on in front of the other. The whole object shown in *Figure VI-6* is about one tenth of a degree in diameter, or about one fifth the diameter of the moon as seen in the sky. But studies of the radio source show it to extend over six degrees or more —12 times the diameter of the moon. That is, the radio emission is coming from a volume of space vastly greater than that occupied by the visible stars and smog. You will remember that this was true for our own galaxy too, as shown in *Figure VI-2*, where the pancake of stars is embedded in a larger, more spherical volume from which radio waves are coming. In the case of Centaurus A the radio-emitting volume is certainly not spherical; it appears like two great plumes extending in opposite directions, with a concentrated radio source at the center of the visible object. Recent observations of it have been made with the radio telescope at Stanford (*Figure VI-3*), with high resolving power. These observations show that this small central radio source of Centaurus A, centered on the object shown in *Figure VI-6*, really consists of two quite separate smaller sources. It may be that here we are detecting material that has been puffed out from an erupting galaxy. In the course of time this material may diffuse into and replenish the extended plumes on each side.

Figure VI-6. The peculiar elliptical galaxy at the center of radio star Centaurus A. The optical object shown here is about one tenth of a degree long, whereas the radio source is 6 degrees across, with two large plumes extending in opposite directions from two small, intense radio stars close together. How this peculiar galaxy, perhaps a pair of galaxies, can produce radio emission far outside its optical body is not yet understood. *Mount Wilson and Palomar Observatories*

Figure VI-7. The close pair of galaxies at the center of radio star Cygnus A. Photographed with the 200-inch telescope, these galaxies are practically at the limit of present optical observation. Yet they apparently are one of the strongest radio sources in the sky. Some astronomers interpret this photograph as two galaxies in collision; others postulate that they are fragments of a gigantic explosion. The radio source is observed to be much larger than the optical images shown.   *Mount Wilson and Palomar Observatories*

Explosions or Collisions of Galaxies?

As already mentioned, Cygnus A is one of the strongest radio sources in the sky. For a long time, optical photographs showed nothing there. Finally, in 1958, Minkowski photographed it with the 200-inch Palomar telescope (*Figure VI-7*). It is about the faintest thing that can be observed optically. Minkowki interprets this object as two galaxies, of about 100 billion stars each, in head-on collision—a catastrophe as tremendous as we can imagine. Shortly after this photograph had been taken, Minkowski was asked, "How can you tell that they really are galaxies in collision?" He replied that, after careful study of the original negative, he saw one galaxy "distorting the other by tidal action." A rival, and completely opposite, interpretation of *Figure VI-7* is that these two galaxies are the fragments of one original galaxy undergoing *fission,* that is, blowing apart in an explosion that must be just as violent as Minkowski's collision. Neither interpretation has been proved as yet, but the widely divergent views on a matter of "observational fact" are typical of the exciting problems on the frontier of research.

If this really is a single galaxy undergoing fission, Cygnus A may be similar to the one with the jet (Virgo A, in *Figure VI-5*), both caught in the act of ejecting material that continues to emit radio waves for some time and might ultimately accumulate in a large plume far from the galaxy. Centaurus A (shown in *Figure VI-6*) has already put out two extensive plumes and is probably putting out two more ejections right now. It may even be a part of the normal development of galaxies to do this —to split themselves in two. This speculation is covered in Chapter VII.

VII

The Life-Story of a Galaxy

Margaret Burbidge

A fairly coherent picture has been built up of the evolution and life-history of single stars; can we make such a coherent picture of the evolution or life-history of a galaxy? At the moment our success is not as clear-cut as in the case of the life-history of a star. For example, you have seen in Chapter VI that there can be opposite points of view about the radio stars; in one interpretation two galaxies are colliding; in the other, a single galaxy is splitting into two parts. At the moment, we have no physical theory or explanation which could fit this second suggestion. In fact, the whole problem of the probable course of evolution of a galaxy is more difficult and complex than for a star. This is not to say that we shall not solve it in the comparatively near future; after all, the evolution of stars was only poorly understood ten years ago. Since then most of the story (Chapters III and IV) has been put together, and who knows what the next ten years will bring to our understanding of the evolution of galaxies.

Chapter V describes the different kinds of galaxies that we see in the sky: spiral galaxies, irregular galaxies without much structure to them, and the smooth ones that we call elliptical galaxies. All these different kinds of galaxies are made up of three components—gas, dust, and stars. There is more gas and dust in irregulars and spirals than in the ellipticals, which have almost none. In trying to trace out the life-history of a galaxy, one way to begin is to look for a time sequence between these different kinds of galaxies. Might one kind of galaxy change into another? If so, which are younger? Which are older?

From Gas to Galaxy

In Chapter V two alternative cosmological theories were described. According to the "Big-Bang" Theory the universe was created at some definite time in the past; matter was then very much closer together in space. Somewhat later all the galaxies might have been formed at one time. By contrast, according to the "Steady-State" Theory, the universe has been about the same all along, and galaxies must be forming now. In either case it is likely that the material out of which the galaxies formed was originally all gas, containing no stars or dust, and spread more or less uniformly throughout space. If a gas is uniformly spread through space, it tends to "clot." If any little fluctuation takes place, one region by chance becoming a bit more dense than another, then the denser region tends to grow, attracting to itself more material by gravitational force. The clots would grow and might easily turn into galaxies.

On this basis, we shall sketch in quite general fashion what might be the life-history of a galaxy—not what can be proved, but what would be reasonable. Starting, then, with a gas spread uniformly throughout all space, fluctuations begin to form what we will call "proto-galaxies." At some stage there will be smaller fluctuations inside a proto-galaxy, and out of these smaller fluctuations stars could form. We will call these "first-generation stars"—the first stars to form in a galaxy—and the gas they formed from might have been pure hydrogen, according to the view that the chemical elements have been built up in the stars, as discussed in Chapter IV. The "Steady-State" Theory, of course, suggests that the gas was not *pure* hydrogen but had a slight mixture of heavier elements ejected from earlier generations of stars and galaxies that had always been around in space.

In either case, the gas that formed the first generation of stars in a new galaxy would have very little of the heavier elements. It would be mostly hydrogen. From the early stages of a star's life discussed in Chapter IV, we know that the more massive a blob of matter that starts condensing, the faster it will contract under its own gravitation to form a star. During contraction, the gas becomes quite hot because of the release of gravitational energy as the gas falls in toward the center. Just as gravitational energy is released in the condensation of a star, so gravitational energy will be released in the formation of a galaxy; therefore the gas at an early stage in the proto-galaxy might be quite hot.

The Youth of a Galaxy

Because the large, hot, blue stars form rapidly, they will generally be imbedded in thinner gas that has not yet condensed into stars. The radiation from these hot stars would cause the gas they are imbedded in to shine quite brightly. Patches of glowing gas like this will show up very well in a galaxy and are seen in many irregular and spiral galaxies. This is the sort of situation we would expect in a young galaxy, and one that we see in the irregular galaxies shown in *Figures V-2* and *VII-1*. There is no pattern; an irregular galaxy is just an unorganized collec-

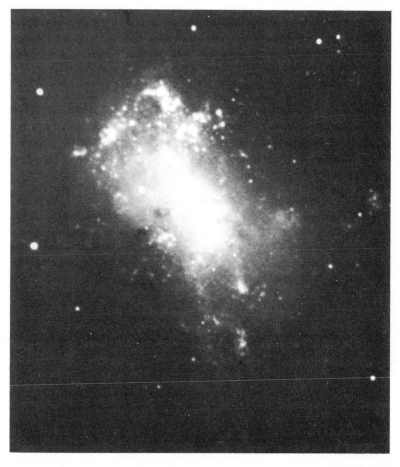

Figure VII-1. An irregular galaxy, NGC 4449. Such an unorganized collection of blue giant stars and blobs of glowing gas is generally considered young in age, since the blue giant stars are expected to be short lived.   *Mount Wilson and Palomar Observatories*

tion of blobs of hot gas shining because they are lit up by massive blue stars imbedded in them. So we might think that an irregular galaxy would be quite young, though there are possible pitfalls in this suggestion, as noted later on.

What would happen next in a young galaxy after the first generation of large, hot stars has formed? These first, massive stars will go through their life-histories fairly quickly, in the manner described in Chapter III, using up all their nuclear fuel. Ten or twenty million years later, at the end of their lives, they should turn into white dwarfs, but they are each so massive that the whole star cannot shrink to a white dwarf without losing a large part of its mass. So these first-generation stars would have to put back into the interstellar material of the galaxy a good deal of the material of which they were made. And this material will have become enriched in the chemical elements "cooked up" in the interiors of the stars: elements such as helium, carbon, nitrogen, and iron.

Some of these heavier elements, once they get out into the space between the stars, can stick together and form dust grains, which pure hydrogen cannot do. (Two hydrogen atoms can stick together in a hydrogen molecule, but these molecules will not form solid dust particles.) And, once the oxygen, carbon, nitrogen, and so on, make dust grains, the gas, now with a mixture of dust in it, can cool. We saw that, in the early history of a galaxy, the gas would be hot; once some dust has formed, the gas can cool because the dust helps the gas to radiate away its heat energy. As the gas in a galaxy becomes cool, the pressure drops and it can fall together—condense under its own gravitational attraction—much more easily and rapidly. Thus it is much easier to form the second and later generations of stars from small density fluctuations.

Order Produced by Rotation

In Chapter V, it was shown that galaxies rotate about their axes. What would happen to an irregular galaxy if it rotates? Could it remain irregular? Star formation is going on, gas is contracting under its own gravitation, and the whole assemblage is rotating as well. We can expect a symmetrical and orderly structure to be produced from this formless mass of material just as a shapely vase can be made of formless clay. It is difficult to make a symmetrical object out of a lump of clay unless you have a potter's wheel to rotate the clay; then it is quite easy. So, we can understand how a galaxy could become more symmetrical-looking from its rotation. An irregular galaxy that started out with relatively few massive blue stars, and no pattern whatever in its structure, would gradually begin to take on a regular, symmetrical shape, with more of the mass collected at the center, and a generally circular outline. The cooling of the gas left over after the stars form would help this gas to contract toward the central or equatorial plane of the galaxy, and soon all of the gas and dust would lie in a thin layer or sheet in the central plane, as described in Chapter VI.

While this was happening—while the new galaxy was shrinking and speeding up its rotation, forming a more regular pattern—star formation would be going on continuously. As each generation of stars forms, the brightest members (which would be the most massive, high-temperature stars) will evolve and go through their lives most rapidly, come to the end stage, and return most of their substance to the space between the stars. But each generation will also contain some stars with a small mass. These small-mass stars, stars like our sun or smaller, with very long lifetimes, will not complete the full cycle that the hot bright stars go through—the cycle from dust to dust and gas to gas. Therefore, there should be a gradual using-up of the material of the galaxy; matter would gradually become locked up in low-mass stars whose lifetimes are so long that they take little part in the interchange between interstellar gas and stars.

Signs of a Galaxy's Age

There are also the stellar remains—skeletons, if you like —the white dwarfs left over after the massive stars have gone through their life cycle. An increasing fraction of the material of the galaxy will gradually get locked up in the form of white dwarfs; and that fraction can take no further part in the interchange between interstellar gas and stars. Thus, the gas in a galaxy will gradually get used up, until eventually there will be none left to form any new stars; in such an aged galaxy we expect only fairly cool stars of small mass, a few red giants into which such stars evolve, and some white dwarfs.

All this suggests that there are indicators of the evolutionary age of a galaxy—things which could be observed and measured from a large distance. We need features that can be measured from great distances if we are to get information about a large part of the universe, and about conditions billions of years ago— for we see the distant galaxies as they were then. We could measure, in the first place, the *color* of a galaxy. In Chapter II we saw how the colors of stars can be measured; the colors of galaxies, which are whole collections of stars, can be measured in the same way. If a galaxy has a red color it is likely to be made up mostly of old stars all of which have a reddish color— stars of a smaller mass than the sun and the red giant stars into which they would evolve. On the other hand, a young, irregular galaxy would have a bluer color because it is largely made up of hot, blue stars. Color thus would be an indicator of the evolutionary age of a galaxy.

We can also measure the *spectrum* of a galaxy, made up of the spectra of all the stars in it—an average or composite spectrum that might reveal the kinds of stars that make up a galaxy.

Another thing to measure is the *mass* of a galaxy, determined by studying how fast it is rotating (Chapter V). Having measured the mass of a galaxy, and the total light it puts out, we can determine the ratio: the mass divided by the luminosity. If we do this for a single star—the sun, for example—we get a certain value of tons mass per billion kilowatts of radiation. For a star cooler than the sun we find that the mass divided by the light is a larger number because of the way in which the luminosity depends so strongly on mass (Chapters III and IV). Stars of low mass put out relatively very little light, whereas stars of high mass are much more spendthrift of their energy. Hence the mass of a galaxy divided by its luminosity is a fairly good indication of the average kind of stars in that galaxy. Of course, it would be better if we could actually study the individual stars, but unfortunately galaxies are so far away that we can only study the brightest individual stars in a few of the nearest ones. What we need is a great deal of information about a very large number of galaxies.

A galaxy that we might think of as being at a somewhat later stage in its life history is shown in *Figure I-10*. This spiral galaxy still has many bright patches in it which we find to be patches of hot gas lit by bright stars. These are spread all through it, just as they are spread through an irregular galaxy. But this spiral has a clearly defined center, a fairly circular outline, and characteristic spiral arms. The color of a spiral like this is a little redder than an irregular galaxy, and from its composite spectrum it seems to have a higher proportion of yellow stars like the sun than does an irregular galaxy. All of this indicates that a loose spiral galaxy is at a later stage in its life-history than an irregular one. *Figure V-1* shows a tighter spiral galaxy (M31) where things have settled down and become still more orderly. M31 looks quite tidy; it has a nice bright little center, then a smooth region, and then the spiral arms neatly wound. Even in a galaxy like M31 there are many patches of gas not yet condensed into stars, which are lit up by nearby hot stars.

Factors that May Influence the Evolution of Galaxies

Finally, the elliptical galaxies in *Figure V-4* are quite smooth. They are much brighter in the center than in their outer parts but they have no bright patches of gas, and seem to be made up entirely of stars. All the gas has been used up. Elliptical galaxies have the reddest color of all, and their composite spectra show that their stars are, on the average, low-mass stars like the sun and the red giants into which such stars evolve. What about the ratio of mass to luminosity? Unfortunately, we do not have much information yet on the masses of elliptical galaxies, but the average for a few shows that they have a much higher ratio of mass to luminosity than the spiral and irregular galaxies. This again suggests that they are at a later stage in their life-history.

Can we now say that an irregular galaxy will turn into a spiral galaxy and, when all the gas is used up, the spiral will turn into an elliptical galaxy? Can we say that we have an evolutionary sequence, irregular types evolving into spirals, and spirals evolving into ellipticals? Harlow Shapley, the famous Harvard astronomer, first suggested about a decade ago that this was happening. But we must keep in mind the warning example set by studies of the evolution of stars. We know that there are many different kinds of stars in the sky, but that we cannot put all these stars into one evolutionary sequence; we

have seen in Chapter IV that the life-histories of stars of different masses are very different. In fact, if we want to make sense
of the life-history of stars, we have to sort the stars first into
groups with the same age but different masses. We cannot say
that a high-temperature, massive star will evolve into a star like
the sun. But in this first attempt at the life-history of a galaxy
we are trying to arrange all the different kinds of galaxies in a
single evolutionary sequence. Perhaps this is not right—perhaps the mass of a galaxy plays an important role in determining
its life-history, just as the mass of a star is very important in its
life-history.

Although we know the masses of only a few galaxies as yet, it
does seem that irregular galaxies and spiral galaxies are, on the
average, less massive than elliptical galaxies. How, then, could
an irregular galaxy become a spiral galaxy and then an elliptical
galaxy, with an *increase* in mass?

There is further evidence from the double galaxies—galaxy
twins, so to speak. For instance, the irregular galaxy M82 lies
quite close in space to the large spiral galaxy, M81, and may
have been formed out of the same general patch of material. It
ought to have the same age, just as the stars in any one cluster
are likely to have the same age. Is the irregular galaxy M82 the
same age as the spiral galaxy M81 near it? M82 is probably a
little less massive than the spiral galaxy M81, but it is rotating,
and before very long it should surely settle down to a spiral
structure. Why is M82 still an irregular galaxy? What stopped
it from becoming a spiral galaxy like M81?

There must be other factors, then, that determine the way in
which a galaxy evolves, beside the mass it had to start with. The
magnetic field is a possible factor, since magnetic fields are
needed (Chapter VI) to explain those galaxies that are radio
sources, and it is quite likely that there are magnetic fields in
all galaxies, including our own. These magnetic fields are quite

small in comparison to the magnetic field on the surface of the earth that causes a compass needle to point north. The magnetic field in our galaxy is only a few hundred-thousandths of this. Nevertheless, a magnetic field of this strength spread out through a whole galaxy involves a great deal of energy.

If magnetic fields are stronger in some galaxies than in others, this might have an effect upon the speed at which interstellar gas could form into stars. A strong magnetic field could delay star formation because magnetic fields tend to "freeze" a conducting gas, making it behave more like a solid, and would tend to keep apart a blob of gas that was about to contract under its own gravitation into a star. In this way the magnetic fields in a galaxy may be important in determining its life-history.

Another factor that might be important is the original *density* of the gas that contracted to form a galaxy. Suppose gas is contracting, and that, before it has achieved high average density, some fluctuations initiate star formation. This might lead to a slower over-all rate of formation than if all the gas forming a galaxy collapsed at once, reaching high density throughout before the first generation of stars formed.

The Origin of S-Zero (So) Galaxies

Another objection to the idea that a spiral galaxy may turn into an elliptical one is connected with *rotation*. Looking at a spiral galaxy edge-on as in *Figure I-11,* we see how flat it is. Elliptical galaxies are never that flat. Once a galaxy has become extremely flat, it is difficult to see how it can round out again, as would be necessary if a spiral galaxy were to evolve into an elliptical galaxy. However, there is a kind of galaxy that has no spiral arms and yet is more flattened than the elliptical galaxies, and these are called So galaxies (see Chapter V). There are many galaxies of this sort in some of the giant clusters of galaxies, and it has been suggested that they were formed by chance collisions. In such a collision the stars of each galaxy just pass each other, simply because there is so much empty space between them. But the interstellar gas and dust clouds in the two galaxies *will* collide, and be separated from the stars. So collisions will sweep the gas out of spirals. S-zero galaxies, which are flat but have no interstellar clouds, might therefore be either the results of collisions between spiral galaxies, or simply aged spiral galaxies that have used up their gas and dust in forming stars.

Figure VII-2 shows an So galaxy in which a small amount of gas remains. You can see that there is a very thin line of dust through the center, the region where the spiral arms used to be. The gas that makes spiral arms is mostly gone, leaving just stars and the remnants of stars.

Winding Up of Spiral Arms

Let us now consider the spiral arms in galaxies. They are fairly symmetrical, and this has a bearing on how they might be "wound up." The central region of a galaxy rotates faster than the outer regions. An early idea about the formation of spiral arms, known as the "coffee-cup" theory, was based on the analogy of a cup of coffee stirred near the middle of the cup. The central part of the coffee goes around faster than the outer parts, and at the rim of the cup the coffee is not moving at all. A little thick cream poured in makes beautiful spiral arms, and it does not matter what shape the blobs of cream start with; the different speeds of rotation will spin them out into spiral shapes.

It is easy, then, to understand how spiral arms are formed by the different rates of rotation in a galaxy; the difficulty is just

Figure VII-2. An So galaxy, NGC 5866. The S-zero (So) type of galaxy is flat like a spiral but shows no spiral arms and is often called a transition stage between spiral and elliptical types. This one has a thin line of dust in it, as a depleted spiral might.

Mount Wilson and Palomar Observatories

the opposite: why don't all galaxies have much more extended spiral arms? If the galaxies are very old they must have rotated a great many times; an average galaxy will rotate, about halfway out from its center, once in perhaps a hundred million years, and will turn a large number of times in its full life (estimated to be ten billion years). We would expect to see spiral arms completely wound up in hundreds of turns, whereas the actual spiral galaxies (*Figures I-10, V-1, V-3*) usually have arms making just one or two turns. It seems that there must be some process that renews or preserves short spiral arms; otherwise the observed rotations of galaxies would wind them out of existence. Here again, it is tempting to assume that magnetic fields stiffen the material of a galaxy and prevent a spiral arm from winding up too far. They may also play some part in the formation or renewing of spiral arms.

In addition to the ordinary spiral galaxies, as noted in Chapter V, there is the class of "barred spirals"—galaxies that have a bar across the center and two spiral arms starting from the ends of the bar (*Figure V-3*). The bar in such a galaxy rotates more or less like a solid wheel, but just beyond the end of the bar the material rotates more slowly so that the arms get trailed out. Something must "freeze" the straight bar into a rigid form so that it does not wind up into spiral arms. But *Figure VII-3* shows a different sort of barred spiral. It has a bar and two large spiral arms, but in the very center there is another little spiral, which turns out to be rotating very fast. It is hard to see how the bar could last very long without getting wound up in the central spiral. There are several other barred spirals like this, and there is a great deal to be learned before we can hope to understand them.

Figure VII-3. A barred spiral galaxy with a spiral nucleus, NGC 1097. A normal barred spiral (SB) galaxy has a straight bar between two spiral arms (*Figure V-3*). The small spiral in the center of this one raises the question of how the bar can remain straight when a part of it is more rapidly rotating at the center.

McDonald Observatory

Are Galaxies Forming Now?

Finally, do we see any galaxies that we think are really young—actually young in years? The "Steady-State" cosmological theory predicts that we should see some galaxies formed very recently; the "Big-Bang" Theory, although it does not say that there could be no young galaxies, must explain them in some special way. *Figure VII-4* shows one of the few galaxies we can claim are fairly young. It is a very odd thing—an ordinary elliptical galaxy accompanied by nearby patches of gas that must have bright, hot stars in them. A galaxy like this could not last very long in its present stage; perhaps this elliptical galaxy, moving through space, captured some left-over material —a blob of gas in which no stars had formed. As a result of the capture, this blob of gas could contract a little, until it was dense enough in some places for stars to form. That is, a young galaxy was formed in the presence of an old one.

Figure VII-5 shows two galaxies rather far away from us and located in one of the big clusters of galaxies, the Coma cluster. A long tail sticks out of the upper galaxy, and another tail from the lower one. You would think such tails must wind up; a tail cannot remain just sticking out into space from a galaxy if that galaxy is rotating at all. And these galaxies are rotating rapidly, as measured by Doppler shifts in their spectra (see Chapter II). That is, a straight, protruding tail makes it very likely that such a galaxy is very young.

Another queer thing is shown in *Figure VII-6;* it looks unlike the galaxies we are used to and yet it certainly is a galaxy. It has two strings of material and a kind of loop. One would expect such an unstable structure soon to change; hence it is also likely to be young.

In summary, it is difficult to understand in detail how one sort of galaxy can evolve into another, yet in a general way we know that it must happen. We know that the stars in a galaxy are ageing (Chapters III and IV), and that the shapes of certain galaxies (*Figures VII-5* and *VII-6*) cannot last, as the motions in each galaxy go on—motions we have measured by Doppler shifts. This reasoning leads us to think that elliptical galaxies are older than spirals and irregular galaxies. But if we go on to

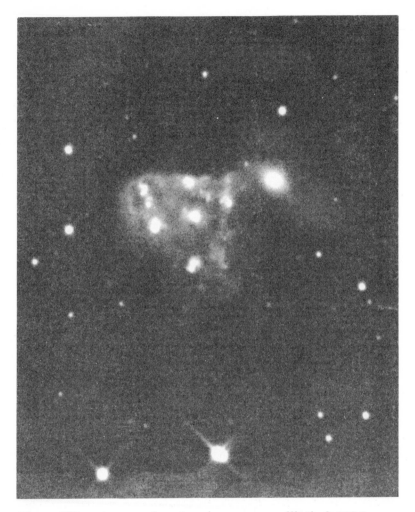

Figure VII-4. A new galaxy forming near an elliptical, NGC 2444, 2445. The bright patches to the left of the normal, presumably old, elliptical galaxy are glowing gas illuminated by young, blue giant stars.   *McDonald Observatory*

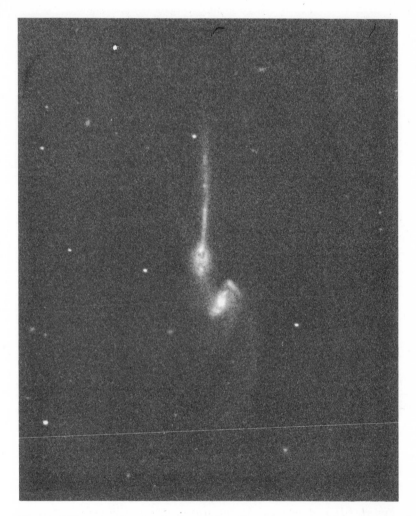

Figure VII-5. A pair of galaxies with tails, NGC 4676. The question here is how the tails can remain sticking out without "winding up" into spiral arms. The spectra show that each galaxy in this pair is rotating rapidly. *McDonald Observatory*

Figure VII-6. A peculiar loop-galaxy, NGC 6621, 6622. Such a shape
fits into no regular class of galaxies; it is a freak that appears to be
unstable and therefore of short life in its present form.

McDonald Observatory

say that all irregular galaxies turn into spirals after 100 million years, and that all spirals turn into ellipticals after a billion years, how can we explain mixed groups or close pairs of one spiral with one elliptical? How can elliptical galaxies be heavier than spirals? (Where did the added mass come from as a galaxy aged?)

One possible explanation is that ageing does not always proceed at the same rate. Perhaps in the "young" spirals we see among "old" ellipticals, something prevented for a long time the formation and ageing of stars. Perhaps the mass of a galaxy has an effect on how rapidly it ages, so that most of the heavy ones have already become "old" ellipticals. Irregular "young" galaxies seen close to "older" spirals or elliptical galaxies suggest that, whatever the cause, evolution goes on at *different rates* in different galaxies even when they are located close to each other in space. Two close galaxies in a double may be at widely different stages in their life-histories, even though they have the same age in years. In fact, there could well be many even younger galaxies that we cannot see—dark blobs of matter in which stars have not yet formed because of magnetic fields or low density or some other peculiar condition. These ideas of the evolution of galaxies can be fitted equally well into either the "Big-Bang" Theory or the "Steady-State" Theory.

From all this you can see that we do not have an adequate theory of how galaxies evolve. More observations and much more theoretical study is needed. The subject of evolution of galaxies is a field in which we can expect great changes in the next few years.

EPILOGUE

How Man Understands the Universe

Thornton Page

At this point it should be clear that the purpose of this book is *not* simply to give facts about the stars and galaxies, how they were formed, how they age, or what the universe will look like 10 billion years from now. The later chapters are intended to show that many of our ideas about the outside universe are imperfect and undergoing rapid change, as is characteristic of the thinking in any active science.

Of course, a puzzled reader may feel that this modern thinking is too *messy*. By contrast, Ptolemy's geared spheres carrying the stars, planets, sun, and moon around us were neat and tidy. One knew where one stood—at the center! It is both unfair and incorrect to say that Ptolemy, Plato, and Aristotle were "wrong"; their theory was consistent with all the observations they could make, as noted in Chapter I. We would scarcely wish to emphasize that Herschel was "wrong" in his early, imperfect idea of the Milky Way Galaxy almost 200 years ago because he did not appreciate its extent, or our off-center position, or the many similar galaxies outside it.

There are many other examples in this book of the rapidly changing concepts of astronomy: 200 years ago, the distances of stars could only be guessed at, and few men questioned their eternal nature; 100 years ago no one had yet conceived of a stellar model; 50 years ago the size of the Milky Way Galaxy was uncertain, and the "age of the universe" was not a specific concept (although Lord Kelvin had argued that the sun could be no older than 10 million years). Even 20 years ago few scientists would have accepted the idea that the abundances of the chemical elements could be changing in time and different in one region of space from those in another. In 1940 radio astronomy had started, but there was as yet no knowledge of a "radio star," or of the cold hydrogen emission of radio waves at 1420 megacycles' frequency. The possibility of making astronomical observations from outside the earth's atmosphere was still a part of science fiction. Only a few nuclear reactions had by then been introduced into calculations of stellar models, and the idea of a star shifting from "hydrogen-burning" to "helium-burning" as a source of nuclear energy had not been thought of. Most of the distances outside the Milky Way Galaxy were reckoned at a fifth of today's values (the "age of the universe" at only 2 billion years), and the continuous creation of matter had not yet been proposed.

Many of the last ten years' advances are covered in the preceding chapters, each of them leading to another problem. For instance, parts of the life-story of a star have been worked out neatly, but some clusters of stars are thus found to have ages exceeding the "age of the universe" in evolutionary cosmology. A cycle has been recognized between the interstellar gas and stars formed from it that later die and return much of their material to the interstellar clouds of gas and dust. This provides the basis for the idea that young, gassy, irregular galaxies evolve into smooth, old, elliptical galaxies that have used up their interstellar gas. But the average elliptical galaxy is found to be many times more massive than the average spiral, and it is unlikely that a galaxy can grow heavier with age. Moreover, the members of close pairs of dissimilar galaxies probably have aged at different rates; possibly the more massive one changes appearance more rapidly than its less massive twin. In fact, the significance of pairs, groups, and clusters of galaxies is only just becoming evident. The question is: Why do so many galaxies occur in groups? The manner of formation of galaxies, whether all at once, as in the Big-Bang Theory, or continuously in time, as in the Steady-State Theory, remains as unsettled as the cosmological model itself.

Yet, in spite of all these changes in our understanding of the universe over several thousand years, there is a unity that cannot be denied. Some will argue that this unity results simply from our selection—from the ideas of the past that we have chosen to relate—but such people ignore the remarkable growth and consistency of scientific thought. Apparently, man is not content to leave his ideas about things he can see—even those as remote as the stars and galaxies—in a "messy," inconsistent state. Nor is he willing to accept the mystical explanation that these remote matters are just the whimsy of the gods.

Thus, in all these efforts to understand stars and galaxies we find, first, the collection of observations; second, the forming of concepts and a theory; third, obtaining more observations as suggested by this theory; and fourth, testing the theory by comparing its predictions with the observations. In Ptolemy's day the observations concerned where the stars, planets, sun, and moon were seen in the sky; the theory involved rotating spheres; and the test was whether these rotating spheres predicted later motions in the sky. Today, the observations concern stars, interstellar gas clouds, galaxies, and radio signals, as well as all the laboratory experiments in physics. One of the theories has to do with slow changes in the composition and appearance of a galaxy. It must be consistent with other tested and accepted theories of stellar evolution and with all the established theories of physics. It will be tested by comparing its predictions with new observations. The use of older, accepted theories is still there, but it is routine. For instance, Ptolemy's celestial sphere serves in mapping optical and radio observations (*Figures V-6* and *VI-2*) and in pointing a telescope at a particular star or galaxy.

Very simply, the drive of research astronomy, as of all science, has always been to make more observations, yet to relate the ones we have in a meaningful theory that (paradoxically) makes unnecessary the further repetition of these observations.

SUGGESTIONS FOR FURTHER READING

I. GENERAL ASTRONOMY

Baker, R. H., *Astronomy*. 7th ed., D. van Nostrand and Co., Inc., Princeton, 1960.

Inglis, S. J., *Planets, Stars and Galaxies*. John Wiley and Sons, Inc., New York, 1961.

Krogdahl, W. S., *The Astronomical Universe; An Introductory Text in College Astronomy*. Rev., The Macmillan Co., New York, 1961.

McLaughlin, D. B., *Introduction to Astronomy*. Houghton Mifflin Co., Boston, 1961.

Struve, Otto, Beverly Lynds, and Helen Pillans, *Elementary Astronomy*. Oxford University Press, New York, 1959.

II. HISTORY OF ASTRONOMY

Munitz, M. K., *Theories of the Universe*. The Free Press, Glencoe, Illinois, 1957.

Pannekoek, Antonie, *A History of Astronomy*. Interscience Publishers, Inc., New York, 1961.

Vaucouleurs, Gerard de, *Discovery of the Universe*. Faber and Faber Ltd., London, 1957.

III. OPTICAL MEANS OF OBSERVATION

Bates, D., *Space Research and Exploration*. Eyre and Spottiswood, London, 1957.

Besserer, C. W., and H. C. Besserer, eds., *Guide to the Space Age*. Prentice-Hall, Inc., Englewood Cliffs, New Jersey, 1959.

Bizony, M. T., ed., *The Space Encyclopaedia*. Artemis Press, London, 1957.

King, H. C., *The History of the Telescope*. Sky Publishing Corp., Cambridge, Mass., 1955.

Kuiper, G. P., and B. M. Middlehurst, eds., *Telescopes*. University of Chicago Press, Chicago, 1960.

Woodbury, D. O., *The Glass Giant of Palomar*. Dodd, Mead and Co., New York, 1953.

IV. Stars and the Milky Way

Bok, B. J., and P. F. Bok, *The Milky Way*. 3rd ed., Harvard University Press, Cambridge, Mass., 1957.

Gaposchkin, C. E., *Stars in the Making*. Harvard University Press, Cambridge, Mass., 1952.

Gaposchkin, C. E., *The Galactic Novae*. Interscience Publishers, Inc., New York, 1957.

Johnson, Martin, *Astronomy of Stellar Energy and Decay*. Faber and Faber Ltd., London, 1949.

Schwarzschild, Martin, *Structure and Evolution of the Stars*. Princeton University Press, Princeton, 1958.

Struve, Otto, *Stellar Evolution; an Exploration from the Observatory*. Princeton University Press, Princeton, 1950.

V. Radio Astronomy

Brown, R. H., and A. L. B. Lovell, *The Exploration of Space by Radio*. Chapman and Hall, London, 1957.

Davies, R. D., and H. P. Palmer, *Radio Studies of the Universe*. D. van Nostrand and Co., Inc., Princeton, 1959.

Menzel, D. H., *The Radio Noise Spectrum*. Harvard University Press, Cambridge, Mass., 1960.

Pawsey, J. L., and R. N. Bracewell, *Radio Astronomy*. Clarendon Press, Oxford, 1955.

Smith, F. G., *Radio Astronomy*. Penguin Books, London, 1960.

VI. Galaxies Outside the Milky Way

Burbidge, E. M., and G. Burbidge, "Stellar Populations," *Scientific American,* Vol. 199, No. 5, November 1958; and "Peculiar Galaxies," *ibid.,* Vol. 204, No. 2, February 1961.

Hubble, E. P., *The Realm of the Nebulae.* Yale University Press, 1936; Dover Publications, Inc., New York, 1958.

Shapley, Harlow, *The Inner Metagalaxy.* Yale University Press, New Haven, 1957.

Shapley, Harlow, *Galaxies.* Rev. ed., Harvard University Press, Cambridge, Mass., 1957.

VII. Cosmology, the Study of the Universe

Bondi, Hermann, *Cosmology.* 2nd ed., Cambridge University Press, New York, 1960.

Bondi, Hermann, et al., *Rival Theories of Cosmology.* Oxford University Press, New York, 1960.

Gamow, George, *The Creation of the Universe.* Rev. ed., Viking Press, New York, 1961.

Hoyle, Fred, *Frontiers of Astronomy.* Heinemann Ltd., London, 1955.

Hoyle, Fred, *The Nature of the Universe.* Rev., B. Blackwell Ltd., Oxford, 1960.

Singh, Jagjit, *Great Ideas and Theories of Modern Cosmology.* Dover Publications, Inc., New York, 1961.

INDEX

SPECTRUM BOOKS

* Also available in limited clothbound edition.

*The American Assembly Series**

* Also available in limited clothbound edition.

Classics in History Series*

Science and Technical Series*

Twentieth Century Views Series*

* Also available in limited clothbound edition.